Rain & Fire

A GUIDE TO

The Last Dragon Chronicles

**For Professor Robert Jahn,
Brenda Dunne – Hug and Hum**
(Nice to know we're not the only scribblers
in the *Margins of Reality*…)

*…and with grateful thanks to
all the crew in LR, BX and NJ:
you know who you are* – wom!

ORCHARD BOOKS
338 Euston Road, London NW1 3BH
Orchard Books Australia
Level 17/207 Kent St, Sydney, NSW 2000

First published in Great Britain in 2010

A Paperback Original

Text © Jay and Chris d'Lacey 2010

The right of Jay and Chris d'Lacey to be identified as the author
of this work have been asserted by them in accordance with
the Copyright, Designs and Patents Act, 1988.
A CIP catalogue record for this book is available
from the British Library.

ISBN 978 1 40831 269 8

3 5 7 9 10 8 6 4 2

Printed in Great Britain

Orchard Books is a division of Hachette Children's Books,
an Hachette UK company

www.hachette.co.uk

For Morgan,

Rain &
Fire

~~from~~

A GUIDE TO

The
Last Dragon
Chronicles

Jay and Chris d'Lacey

ORCHARD

"Stories float around like snowflakes, don't they?
They settle on the ears of anyone who'll listen."

Zanna (from *Fire Star*)

CONTENTS

Hello, and a warm welcome to you all. *Hrrr!*

Packed within these covers is a huge amount of information about Chris d'Lacey, his life as an author and the first five books in his fantasy series *The Last Dragon Chronicles*. As his wife and business partner, you can be assured that what you discover herein is accurate and authentic and much of it is material that you will not be able to find elsewhere – but this is no dry academic tome to be pored over in some dark and dusty tower. This is a book that can be read from start to finish, like any other, but equally it can be opened at random – for wherever you dip in, you will find snippets of interest to hold your attention, anecdotes to make you laugh, or background history to share with your friends.

This, then, is the inside story of *The Last Dragon Chronicles*, so far:

The Fire Within
Icefire
Fire Star
The Fire Eternal
Dark Fire

Jay d'Lacey, Brixham, 2010

Imagine you were a young man, twenty years old and just starting out on a journey of independence. You want to leave home to go to college to take a degree in…let's say Geography. You apply to a number of places, probably not Oxford or Cambridge because they're a little too highbrow for someone like you, who tends to get a bit confused by too much learning, and you're happily accepted by a small college with a decent reputation in a more provincial part of the country. In a moment, we'll give it a name.

Having found your place of learning you need to arrange some accommodation. There are no living quarters at the college itself, so you need to apply to one of the halls of residence nearby. However, because you've been slow to read the paperwork (or more likely mislaid it), all the halls are full. Lectures begin in a few days' time. You need to find somewhere else to stay – and fast.

So waving goodbye to your home town, Blackburn, you hop onto a train and head south-east. Where you're going is a fair old distance away. You'll probably fall asleep with your nose against the window and snore, to the annoyance of everyone in the carriage.

Fortunately, you're in no danger of missing your stop because the train terminates in London, where you have to change. Time for a sandwich and a cup of coffee while you wait on a short, fairly isolated platform for your connection into the suburbs.

The train that turns up is nothing like the express that brought you this far. It's a little dingy (inside and out). It rattles. The carriages move like a broken concertina. The people in the carriages talk with a different accent from yours and none of them seem to be in any kind of hurry. The same could be said of the train itself. It stops every few minutes at stations that are becoming ever more rural. The grey, industrial streets of London have given way to green fields, hedgerows and trees. It's autumn, so the leaves are turning russet and brown, but most of them are clinging to their branches for now. You see churches, parks, the occasional stretch of water. Narrower roads. Old-fashioned telephone boxes. People wobbling around on bicycles. The houses are redbrick, clustered into towns. One of these is going to be your destination.

When the train pulls in, the only person to alight is you. No one checks your ticket; it's not that kind of place. Slinging your one bag over your shoulder, out through the barrier you go.

From a grubby little man at a newsstand on the High Street, you buy the afternoon edition of the *Scrubbley Evening Echo*. You flip to the pages listing places to rent. What you see there doesn't look good. Everywhere is *incredibly* expensive. The paltry set of banknotes you've stashed in your wallet are now cowering somewhere deep in your pocket. They would barely fund a week in any of these places. All you would be able to afford to eat would be a can of baked beans – and you'd have to make them last. Just to make matters worse, a lively autumn breeze lifts the paper from your fingers and carries it down the length of the High Street. It flies into the face of a large black Doberman. The dog doesn't look pleased. You decide to move on.

As you stroll up the High Street, you come to an opening between the rows of shops. A precinct of some sort, with a large white building at the far end. Beyond it you can see a huddle of trees. You feel drawn to go and look at them. *Powerfully* drawn, but you don't know why. Right beside you is a signpost, complete with blue signs. The big white building turns out to be a library. The trees are the Scrubbley Library Gardens. You stare down the precinct, looking slightly lost. Strangely, you feel as if you've only just awoken. As if everything that has gone before simply doesn't matter. As if nothing even existed before this day.

"Hello. Are you lost?" A little old lady with a shopping trolley is tugging your sleeve.

"I'm, erm, looking for…tourist information," you say, noting there's a blue sign pointing up the High Street. The old lady points in the opposite direction. But then old ladies are like that sometimes.

The Tourist Information Centre is a yellow stone building at the intersection of roads leading out of town. Perhaps they can provide you with a list of places known to be used for student accommodation. Well, they might if they were open. It's Wednesday afternoon. Half-day closing. Your shoulders sag. This adventure is not going well.

Sighing, you sit down on the steps of the closed TIC with your bag upon your knees and your chin upon your bag. People pass. They look at you. They smile. They wonder, perhaps, if you shouldn't have a collecting box by your feet and a wire-haired dog on a blanket beside you. The thought of hanging a sign around your neck saying 'GOOD HOME WANTED' does pass through your mind, just as a Post Office van pulls up nearby. Idly, you watch the postie unlock the post box and scoop the cascading letters into a sack. He locks the box up again and throws the sack of letters into the van. Then he roars off into the countryside.

12

That's when you see that he's missed a letter. It's in the gutter at the foot of the box, in danger of being franked by dozens of car tyres. So hauling your bag onto your shoulder once more, you step into the road and pick up the letter. This will be your token good deed for the day. *Tink*. Back into the box it goes. Bye-bye, letter. Have a nice journey. You shrug and turn around. This random act of kindness has left you standing outside a newsagent's shop. Nothing special about that, you think. But in the window of the shop is a board full of postcards. Right away, your eye is drawn to this:

Lodgings Available - £40 per week

Nice room in pleasant family house
Meals and laundry included
Suit clean, tidy, quiet student

Please write to: Mrs Elizabeth Pennykettle, 42 Wayward Crescent, Scrubbley

PS Must like children and cats

and dragons...

Forty pounds a week. That's more like it. But wait a moment, you have to *write*? You do have some writing things in your bag, but you don't have time to post a letter, catch a train home and wait for a reply. But the Universe hasn't brought you this far for nothing. Already, an idea is brewing in your mind.

You go into the paper shop and ask for directions. Wayward Crescent, the man says, is about a mile away, just off the main Scrubbley road. Turn right, after

Calhoun's General Store. Fifteen minutes, at a brisk walk.

Smiling, you go outside and open your bag. You find a bench and spread a writing pad over your knee.

Dear Mrs Pennykettle,

Help! I am desperately in need of somewhere to stay. Next week, I am due to start a Geography course at Scrubbley College and I haven't been able to find any lodgings.

I am scrupulously clean, and as tidy as anyone of my age (20) can be. My hobby is reading, which is generally pretty quiet. I get along very well with children and I love cats.

Yours sincerely,

Mr David Rain

PS I'm afraid I haven't seen any dragons about of late. I hope this isn't a problem.

That last part. The bit about dragons. That was weird. Better dragons than spiders, though. Or mice. Or aubergines.

You're wasting time. Away you go. At a brisk pace. Brisker than brisk. You're out of breath by the time you reach Calhoun's, but this is partly due to excitement now.

The Crescent is quiet. A sleepy little backwater, lined with mature trees. The sound of birds and motor mowers is in the air. Number 42 is close to one end. Semi-detached with number 41. It's perfect. The ideal suburban residence. Bit of a hike from Scrubbley College, but let's face it, you need the exercise.

You tiptoe down the drive, up to the door. You push your letter through, making sure the flap rattles. Then you step aside quickly so you can't be seen.

"I'll get it," cries a woman's voice.

Mrs Pennykettle, presumably. You knock your fists together. They're in. Success!

There's a pause. You hear the sound of ripping. She's opening the envelope, reading the letter now. How long would it take? Thirty seconds? Forty? You give it fifty, with elephants in between. Then you present yourself at the door. You take a deep breath and aim your finger at the bell…and almost poke your would-be landlady in the eye.

Because she's opened the door already.

"Oh," you say. That wasn't supposed to happen.

She looks at you carefully, but before she speaks she glances at a small green dragon sculpture that's sitting on a shelf just inside the door. "Mmm," she says, as if the dragon might have whispered something important. Then she relaxes and says, "Hello, David."

"Erm, hello," you mutter. You want to blink, but it's hard to take your eyes off this amazing woman. She's not classically beautiful, but she is stunning. Piercing green eyes and a mane of red hair, plucked from at least three lions. She doesn't seem at all fazed by what you've done. But how did she know to open the door?

"Would you like to come in?"

"It's about the room," you say, rather awkwardly. You feel that you ought to explain yourself, at least.

She smiles and says, "I know. I got your letter." She waggles it and once again looks at the dragon.

Is that thing *frowning*, you wonder?

"Please," she says, opening the door a little wider. So you step into the hall. And the first thing you notice are the dragons in the window recess, halfway up the stairs. There's another one peeking through the banister rails. And another on the potted fern you've just brushed past. Little clay sculptures. All over the place. And all of them are looking at you.

Behind you, the front door closes softly. And you may think this is where the journey ends, but the truth is it's really only just beginning. An incredible journey of love and legends, adventure and magick. In a voice like a wind from another world, Mrs Pennykettle says from behind your back, "Welcome to Wayward Crescent, David. We've been expecting you…"

Chris d'Lacey, Autumn 2010

Chapter 1: The Dawn of Dragons

The existence of dragons

Chris recently found an article on the Internet stating that if you compared the history of Earth with a calendar year, then the first cell of anything that could be called 'life' did not appear until mid-summer. Plants followed in August, then the various animals in the next few months. Dinosaurs arrived at the winter solstice, around 21st December, and died out by Boxing Day, the 26th. Man didn't appear until early evening of the 31st, and true civilisation not until four minutes to midnight. Allegedly, many living species became extinct 'daily' – '*including dragons*', he thought, in a blinding flash of inspiration.

Now, I don't know about you, but to him that is a very exciting concept. Not that dragons died out, of course, but that they might actually have existed in the first place on this wonderful blue planet of ours. Imagine seeing a group of them (a flock? a wing? a *flame*?) soaring and swooping overhead in the warmth of the sun. Or beating their huge majestic wings against a fierce Arctic gale. Would you be scared silly or would you be exhilarated? Would you rush outside to stare in wonder at the spectacle, or would you cower indoors, too terrified to even peek through the window?

Or would you be so used to seeing them around that you would just accept their presence and go about your normal day without paying them much attention? These are some of the questions that Chris wanted to find his own answers to when he wrote *The Last Dragon Chronicles*.

He is often asked whether he believes that dragons did exist on this world, and he usually replies, 'I'd like to.' He is in very good company. From doing some background reading, I found that while relatively few people do believe in their one-time existence, a large majority, just like Chris, 'would like to'. What can it be about dragons that fires (sorry!) the imagination so strongly? Especially since, overall, they have had a pretty duff press.

Think of most dragon legends and myths; nine times out of ten they seem to feature dragons as the bad guys – fire-breathing monsters who would have you for dinner as soon as look at you. Personally, I reckon all this was a ploy to keep knights in shining armour in work. What else could they do, after all, apart from rescue helpless damsels in distress? No damsels, no job. To be fair, there are some cultures around the world who do revere dragons and think them admirable creatures, *and* most definitely believe that they were real. China is the most notable example, Vietnam another, and much closer to home, Wales has its own red dragon.

But love them or loathe them, they do seem to pop up in so many countries' legends that you have to think that there is something in it. 'No smoke without fire' comes to mind – a highly appropriate phrase, in the circumstances.

Perhaps there is a common folk memory or group recall from way back, or maybe it is all simply wishful thinking, that we feel that there somehow just 'ought' to be dragons, to fulfil some unacknowledged and unconscious need in us all. Or, to stretch the imagination a little further, could it be that they did (still do?) exist, but on some other world, and that there was a bleed-through or crossover to this one in the dim and distant past, mentally and emotionally, if not physically? Whichever way, dragons do seem to be 'hard-wired into the human consciousness'. I don't know who came up with that phrase, but I think it sums it all up beautifully.

Chris d'Lacey's dragons

Although there is this huge fascination with dragons, Chris himself, when asked, always used to say that he wasn't particularly smitten with them in his early years; never gave them much thought. However, on closer questioning for this book, I discovered that one of his all-time favourite books from childhood is *The Hobbit* by J. R. R. Tolkien. And guess who one of the main characters is? Smaug, a classic 'bad' dragon who sits on his pile of stolen treasure and roars vengeance on anyone who dares to intrude upon him. The edition that we have even has Smaug defending his ill-gotten gains on the cover. A subtle influence there, perhaps, after all.

Chris's current take on dragons is that they are noble beasts, worthy of respect and awe, spiritual guardians of the planet and servants and defenders of Gaia, Mother Earth. But Chris does not limit himself to one 'type' of dragon; in *The Last Dragon Chronicles*, there are two very different sorts (one large, one small; both benevolent). The first, as you might expect, are the *relatively* traditional 'real' dragons; full-sized, immensely powerful, fire-breathing and truly awesome. But they are birthed from eggs by parthenogenesis...

The second type are more unusual still. They are about eight to ten inches high and made from clay by one of the main characters, a potter called Elizabeth Pennykettle. She sometimes uses something called 'icefire' in the process, which makes them into 'special' dragons, that is, ones that can come alive. All the dragons speak variants of a language called dragontongue, as do Liz and her daughter, Lucy, as well as the odd polar bear or two. (Yes, that's right, polar bears. I'll come to those a bit later.) These small dragons are to be found all around the Pennykettles' home, from the entrance hall to the 'Dragons' Den', where they are created.

David Rain, the hero of the series, even has a wee in the Pennykettles' bathroom with a small 'puffler' dragon named Gloria sitting on the loo cistern in front of him. She's there to 'puffle' a pleasant rose scent when necessary. David does have the grace to turn her to face the wall – but whether to spare her blushes or his own, who can say?

Each of the special clay dragons that Liz creates has a particular talent or ability. There is a wishing dragon, a guard dragon (who is rather young and inexperienced and therefore always needing to check his manual for the correct procedure), a natural healing dragon, and many more. But the one you most need to know about is Gadzooks. 'Zookie' is made especially for David as a housewarming gift when he comes to lodge in the Pennykettle household, and he is an inspirational writing dragon. Gadzooks helps David get unstuck when faced with any problem – particularly writers' block. This is just as well, as David, like Chris, eventually becomes a writer...

ears: can reach the size of large rose petals in a listening dragon

top knot: a sign of dragonliness

eyes: violet when active, green when solid and fooling humans

eye ridges: often raised in confusion...

'trumpet-shaped' nostrils: excellent for blowing smoke rings

paws: more nimble than they look, largest in a wishing dragon (like this one) →

stiff, zig-zagging scales down the spine: where dragons like to be tickled...

scales: normally green, and layered like roof slates, but can vary a lot

big flat feet: evolved after years of 'stamping about'

the tail: the final arrow-shaped scale is called an 'isoscele', which is thought to possess magical powers

The anatomy of a Pennykettle dragon

Chapter 2: From Small Acorns…

London bound

Chris had just finished university, and was working in his dad's pub, the White Horse, whilst sorting out what he wanted to do with his life, when a friend persuaded him to move to London. The friend promised to find Chris somewhere to live and, taking up the offer, Chris soon found himself on a fast train down to the capital, followed by a slower one out to the suburbs, and ultimately knocking on the door of his new landlady in Bromley, Kent. Not at all unlike David Rain, in fact, although there were no 'children, cats or dragons' involved in Chris's case. He settled in quite readily and got on well with the family with whom he was lodging.

Making new friends, though, he thought would be quite tricky, as he was still unemployed. He regularly went into the centre of the town, usually on foot due to a lack of money and a desire to get to know the area, which was entirely new to him. The outskirts of Bromley are quite leafy, but the town itself much less so, with one notable exception: the Churchill Library Gardens. Chris discovered the library quite early on – one of his favourite things to do was to take a book out and wander through the public gardens alongside until he found a sunny spot, whereupon he would sit on a wall next to a path overlooking a large stand of trees. Once settled, book in one hand, sandwich in the other, he would while away the day until it was time to go back to his digs.

One day, as he was doing exactly that, a squirrel suddenly turned up on the path nearby. It sat up on its hind legs, twitched its nose and tail, which Chris took to mean 'anything for me, please?' and waited patiently. Being a generous sort of chap, but having only a small corner of sandwich left, he offered the squirrel that. The squirrel took it with great glee, twiddled it round in its paws a few times and popped it into its mouth. Yum. But no – categorically not 'yum' *at all* – as fast as the sandwich went in, out it came again. It was at this point that Chris discovered that squirrels can look totally disgusted. Off it went, shaking its head and spitting *puh, puh, puhhh*, every few steps. Rather taken aback by this vehement display of ingratitude, Chris was forced to the conclusion that squirrels are not terribly keen on cheese and pickle sandwiches.

Thinking no more of the incident, he shrugged his shoulders and turned his attention back to his book. Eventually, this being October, it got a little chilly. Home time. Chris mostly took the same route back to his lodgings – it was the shortest and therefore the quickest way – but for whatever reason, on this day he found himself veering from the usual path and taking one in a slightly different direction. Such a small deviation, such a tiny decision, and yet, unbeknown to Chris, the wheels of the Universe had turned and a step was taken towards his destiny.

This new way happened to take Chris past a large oak tree. It had shed its abundant crop of acorns all over the pavement and far into the road. Chris was unaware of this until a car, coming too fast around the bend, sprayed him like a scatter gun with the acorns that had caught under its tyres. Jolted out of his reverie, the bright idea suddenly came to him. *This is what squirrels like to eat. Acorns, not cheese and pickle sandwiches…*

Acorns

The next day, he returned to the spot under the oak and gathered up every acorn he could find. Then, laden with two large brown paper bags full of squirrel delight, he retraced his steps to the library gardens and settled down in the same place as the day before. He didn't have long to wait. Within minutes, the same squirrel appeared on the path by his side. Chris was sure of it. Perhaps it was just the play of shadows on its face in the autumn sunshine, but it definitely seemed to *wink* at him in a knowing way. Slightly disturbed by this, but determined to make up for his sandwich faux pas, he tentatively offered up an acorn. The squirrel took one open-eyed look, made a fast grab for it, and guzzled it on the spot. Success!

The squirrel thought so too. It sat wide-eyed and waiting. Chris obliged with another nut. This time the creature twizzled it in its paws as before, but then ran across the pathway and between some railings, burying the acorn in the loose soil to be found there. That done, it immediately came back for 'thirds'. Once more Chris obliged. The squirrel ran up a nearby tree and deposited the acorn somewhere within a hole in one of the branches, promptly returning for another go, obviously thinking all its Christmases must have come at once. However, when it reached Chris this time, a second squirrel was being fed a nut. Then a third, a fourth, a fifth arrived...until within a very short space of time there were no less than seventeen squirrels all feasting and scrabbling around Chris's feet. Some of the tamer ones even plucked up enough courage to run up his legs and perch on his lap, the bravest of all sticking its furry little head right into his greatcoat pocket. He'd certainly made a lot of new friends – and much quicker than he'd expected!

At this point a woman pushing a baby buggy came along the path, holding the hand of a young girl of four or five. They stopped to watch the scene before them. The young girl pointed and in a piping little voice said, "Ooh, look, Mummy. It's the squiwwel man." And so it turned out to be, but many more years were to pass before the world at large became aware of that fact.

The start of something...

Ten years later, Chris was working as a lab technician at Leicester University Medical School and, being a keen songwriter, was writing and recording in his spare time. However, with full-time employment, there wasn't much of that available. Looking to find a less energy-intensive way of expressing his creativity, he decided to drop the music temporarily and focus on just the words. *Writing*, he thought. *How difficult can that be?* Ha! Famous last words, almost. His office waste bin (and the surrounding area) quickly filled up with scrunched-up bits of paper. Failed attempts at a science fiction short story. Failed attempts at short, long, middling, *any* kinds of story. Frustration reigned. But Chris is nothing if not persistent. He decided as a final try to write a cutesy little tale as a Christmas present for me. Romantic soul, eh?

For a previous Christmas present, Chris had bought me a polar bear soft toy, which he'd put outside in the back garden, leaving him with one paw raised against the back door, as if he was knocking. Chris's story was to be something very simple; how Boley the polar bear had arrived in our back garden from the North Pole. Easy.

Christmas present extraordinaire

But no, not easy. Chris had barely got two paragraphs written when he realised that he knew nothing about polar bears except that they were white and lived at the North Pole. Wrong on both counts, actually – their hair is hollow, and is more of a cream colour because of it; and they live right across the Arctic ice cap – *except* at the Pole. Oh well. A trip to the local library was called for. Mission achieved, Chris returned home with a book called *The World of the Polar Bear* by Thor Larsen, intending to cherry-pick a few interesting snippets to dot around the cutesy little tale. He began writing. And writing. And writing. The tale took two and a half years to complete. All *250,000 words* of it. Six hundred A4 pages; longhand.

I remember this very well; I typed it.

This *little tale*, if nothing else, taught Chris the craft of writing. It was ultimately named *White Fire*, and parts of it were used in the dragon books, as if written by David Rain, who also writes a book called *White Fire*. It should be stressed, however, that the two books are not the same. David's is an ecological plea to save polar bears and the planet; Chris's goes much further than that, being a grand saga involving the Inuit people, white men (researchers, hunters, etc.) from the south, and great dynasties of polar bears. It has never seen the light of day and remains dormant in a desk drawer, awaiting – who knows what?

'White fire' is a metaphor for spirituality, and set the seed for the dragon books. It was written partly at home, early mornings and late evenings, and partly in Chris's tea breaks at the University. It was written longhand because (believe it or not) this was still in an age when computers were few and far between. Chris's whole department had only one, for instance. He eventually 'graduated' to using this machine, but until that time, his trusty pen and pad were his tools of the trade. It became a standing joke among his colleagues that Chris wouldn't be going along to the tea room with them, he would be, 'writing his best-selling novel, ha ha.'

One day, one such colleague walked into the room where the computer was housed and said, "Still writing about polar bears? Can't you write about anything else?"

Chris stopped, left a blank line, and began, 'It was a beautiful autumn morning in the library gardens…'

To this day, he does not know why he did this – or

where it came from. He refers to it as his 'Tolkien moment'. (Apparently J. R. R. Tolkien, a professor at the time he wrote *The Hobbit*, and marking exam papers, came upon a blank sheet of paper within the pile. It is alleged that he, for no apparent reason, wrote: 'In a hole in the ground there lived a hobbit.' Of such moments careers are made.)

Squirrels

"What's that about?" chimed said colleague.

"I think it's about squirrels," Chris replied, mystified.

Exit colleague, guffawing to all within earshot, "You won't believe this! He's writing about squirrels now!" Gales of laughter ensued.

By now, however, Chris was beginning to appreciate the importance of such inspirational moments and he followed the idea up. The story poured out in a phenomenal rush. He decided to take a break from *White Fire* as he realised that, at this speed, he could probably write the squirrel story as my Christmas present instead as clearly, the polar bear one would not now be finished in time.

Knowing nothing about this intended gift (I was very ill at that juncture and slept heavily because of it), I snoozed on unawares whilst Chris got up extra early in the mornings, trogged across the local park to the

Uni, wrote another chapter of the book, returned home, brought me a cup of tea, (still with his outdoor coat on – I assumed he was just off to work, rather than returning from it), had breakfast and then went back to work for the normal start of the day. Bless him, he kept this up for over two months. And I got my story.

The inspiration for its setting was the Churchill Library Gardens in Bromley. Chris had always retrospectively felt guilty for gathering up all the acorns by the roadside on his way home that far-off day, as he later realised that although he had been helping the squirrels in the gardens, he had almost certainly also been depriving those around the tree of their own 'harvest'. He therefore wrote the storyline the reverse way round – the acorns were stolen *from* the library gardens to be 'donated' elsewhere, in fact to trap and subsequently aid an injured squirrel called Conker. Quite an ethical chap, then, after all.

The library gardens, Scrubbley – or should that be Bromley?

The story (entitled *The Adventures of Snigger the Squirrel*) begins with Snigger and the rest of the library gardens' squirrels waking up one morning expecting to find a huge nutfall, as it has been very windy indeed the night before. However, upon reaching the clearing where the abundance of acorns should have been, it is clear that something terrible has happened because there is not a sign of a single nut anywhere…

"But where are they all?" said Snigger, astonished to find that the ground was not carpeted with the fruit of the tree, as in previous years.

A female squirrel, Cherrylea, replied, "There was a nutfall. There was. I saw it… Last night, the eve of nutfall, I lay tossing and turning in my drey, too excited by the prospect of the forthcoming harvest to sleep. I'm sure many of you were the same way." Several heads nodded in support. Cherrylea continued: "As you know, my drey overlooks the clearing. For much of the night I could hear the wind whistling through the branches, wrapping itself around them and shaking the acorns clear. Down they came like raindrops on the pond, plopping into the leaf-fall below in such numbers that I was tempted to leave the drey right then and begin the harvest by the beam of the lamplight that shines through the dark hours… But knowing that would be unfair to those of you who drey over the hill, I resisted all such temptation."

Cherrylea swallowed hard, her mouth dry with fear, her

tail twitching nervously. "I did leave my drey last night,"
she began, "but I only went as far as the old stump tree,"
she added loudly, referring to a large sycamore that had had
several branches sawn in half some years before to prevent
them crashing through the windows of the library building.
"I was so excited. I knew there would be nuts everywhere.
Everywhere!" she said, opening out her short front legs and
doing a little turn to indicate the extent of the fall. "I was
about to run back to my drey when suddenly a great dark
shadow spread all across the ground where we are now
standing." The squirrels looked nervously about them, some
moved closer to their friends. "I was very frightened... The
last thing I remember before fleeing to my drey was seeing
a horrid black beast scuffling about among the
leaves...collecting up our nutfall."

The 'horrid black beast', or rather *nutbeast*, that
Cherrylea refers to is, of course, a man, dressed in a long
black greatcoat...and this is the first appearance of the
character who, much later, became David Rain, the
hero of *The Last Dragon Chronicles*.

Chapter 3: ...To Grand Dragons

Writing for children

Over the next few years, Chris finished *White Fire*, and then found he could turn his hand to other genres and other lengths of story at will. He wrote short stories for adults and had some reasonable success, being published regularly in small-press magazines, and receiving excellent feedback from the writing competitions he entered, but few prizes.

One day, a friend at the local writers' group that he attended (and still does, nearly thirty years on) gave him a leaflet for a competition to write for children. It was to be a story of 3,000 words, the prize was £2000 and the winner and eleven runners-up were to be published in an anthology. Up to this point, Chris had not tried his hand at writing for children at all. He thought he would give it a go. How hard could it be? Very, is the answer to that one. Very, very, very.

He was back to crumpling paper in frustration, though that was more difficult to do, now that he had progressed to using a computer and printer. Thus several rainforests were saved in the d'Lacey household by the advent of modern technology. He continued to struggle with writing (or rather, *not* writing) this story. He hummed, he hawed, he pondered, he wailed.

The deadline was looming; up popped an idea.

He had a story called *Ice*, written for adults, with an environmental theme: the hole in the ozone layer, which was very current at that time. But Chris had never been able to sell it. If he changed it around so that it was told through the eyes of a child, maybe it would work...

He rewrote the story. He entered the competition. He didn't win. Or get into the anthology. *Ah well, that's me done with kids' stuff,* he thought, but he read it out to his writer friends and one of them suggested he send it to a publisher. He did some research and sent off his manuscript. A while later he received a phone call from a lovely lady saying she would like to buy his story. Knowing no better, he was very pleased, but that's all. If Chris had known then how incredibly difficult it is to get picked up off what is called the 'slush pile' (that is the pile of unsolicited manuscripts sent in by hopeful would-be authors), he might have just decided to stay in bed. Or juggle with his socks. Or coochie the cat.

Nevertheless, at thirty-nine-and-three-quarters years old, *A Hole at the Pole,* as it was subsequently named, became his first published book. One book does not a children's author make. However, on the strength of it, Chris managed to get a literary agent, and further children's books got written – and published. They were all for quite young children, but his agent suggested that he attempt a longer work, a novel, for a slightly older age group.

Chris suggested she look at *Snigger*. But 'talking animal' books were not in vogue, so that got a thumbs down. Could he rework it? Turn it around so it was told from the viewpoint of humans? Would that help? Perhaps a character, let's call him David, could come to lodge with a mum-and-daughter single-parent family? The daughter would be squirrel-mad, and want him to help her save an injured one that was running around in the garden. David would be the 'nutbeast' who 'steals' the nutfall to attempt to catch – Conker, of course. The rewrite took place. As did the definitive rejection thereof, almost immediately afterwards. Once again, *Snigger* was shelved and set aside.

In the fullness of time, Chris changed agent, and did write his first children's novel. It was called *Fly, Cherokee, Fly* about a young boy who finds an injured pigeon in a local park, exactly as Chris and I had done several years previously. He nurses it back to health against a background of bullying in and out of school. 'Our' pigeon was a feral, or common street bird; Darryl, the boy in the story, finds a racing pigeon. *Cherokee* was shortlisted for a prize called the Carnegie Medal, one of the highest honours in children's fiction. It didn't win, but was 'highly commended', in other words, it came second.

Back to *Snigger*

After the success of *Cherokee*, Chris was looking around for another idea for a new novel when his then editor, Megan Larkin, left to take up a position with a different publisher. They stayed in touch, though, becoming good friends. Eventually Chris plucked up courage enough to show Megan the rewritten squirrel story, now renamed *Snigger and the Nutbeast*. Overall, Megan liked the story, but felt it was lacking in certain areas. Among many very good suggestions she offered to make it a better book was that of giving the mother in the story a job. Megan didn't feel that taking in a lodger would provide enough income for a single-parent family. Chris agreed, but was at a loss as to what 'Mrs Pennykettle' could do. He knew that he wanted it to be somewhat artistic or creative, and done from home. Nothing suggested itself, but there was no rush. The Universe would provide in its own good time.

It did. It provided a cheery lady called Val Chivers. Val, along with her husband, Peter, has become a firm friend over the years, but we weren't to know that on that chilly weekend so long ago. Chris and I had a rare day off: we decided to go to a local craft fair at a place called Stoughton Farm Park. There were the usual stalls – lavender cushions, wheat bags, jewellery, wooden toys. And then there were dragons.

*Val Chivers creating her
amazing dragons*

Val's fabulous and wonderfully inventive clay dragons. They were green, mostly; a few bluer than green. Eight to ten inches high, *gorgeous*. We couldn't take our eyes off them. But in those days we were broke most of the time, and although the dragons weren't expensive, we couldn't possibly afford one.

Val saw us looking longingly and started up a conversation during which we explained our plight. Perhaps she could put one aside for us until we could get enough money together to buy it? Instead, Val pointed us towards a corner of the stall we hadn't noticed: 'Casualty Corner'. Here were dragons with slight imperfections – missing toes, chipped spines, streaky glaze. For five pounds. That we could afford.

I raised my head in delight, only to lock eyes with the dragon we just knew was ours. We paid for him and said a happy goodbye to Val, never thinking that we would see her again. In the car on the way back home I held our new companion in my lap. Having been chatting about our day, we stopped at some traffic lights, where Chris suddenly yelled out, "She's a potter! Elizabeth Pennykettle is a potter and she makes clay dragons which she sells at the local market. And she has them dotted all around the house as ornaments." The small clay dragon twitched his tail on my knee, I swear it.

This minor revelation, among many other changes, was written into *Snigger* and duly sent back to Megan for her approval. Megan definitely saw the potential in the story. She had one more comment to make: "Can we do something more with the dragons?" she said, quite innocently. *"Can they come to life?"*

Chris burst out laughing on the phone. "If they come to life, it will be a fantasy story, not the animal rescue story you wanted me to write." Megan was adamant. Dragons in, squirrels out. But after all this time, Chris was not about to give up on *Snigger*. "If I can find a legitimate way to keep the squirrels in it, while shifting the emphasis to dragons, can I do it?"

Megan was swayed somewhat, but reserved the right to say 'no' if she wasn't convinced. Chris began the mammoth task of a wholesale rewrite once more. It took months. But eventually the dragons were woven in throughout the whole manuscript. Once the concept of 'living' dragons was accepted, they did indeed seem to have lives – and abilities – of their own. It helped that we remembered that Val had created different characters for her clay dragons. Ones with large 'ears': in Chris's mind they became 'listening dragons'. One with a bunch of flowers became a 'potions' dragon, able to 'fluence' people by getting them to sniff her bouquet. Another had overlarge paws – now a 'wishing' dragon, and so on. Other characters, created by us, have then been used by Val to create further varieties of dragons for sale. Thus she has made Gollygosh Golightly, for instance, who carries a magical toolbox. More of him later, in the 'Who's Who' chapter.

However, the most relevant dragon, the one we purchased initially and named Gadzooks (the best fiver we have *ever* spent), turned out to be the key to retaining the squirrels in the story in a very natural way. As we perceived him, he had a notepad and pencil in his paws – an inspirational writing dragon, obviously. So Chris had 'David' write a story, within Chris's own story, for Lucy Pennykettle's eleventh birthday present, Gadzooks helping him when he gets stuck. David reads parts of it to Lucy throughout the latter part of Chris's book. Success at last! Megan liked it, and it was to be published.

Just the beginning

Book covers are generally thought out and produced long before the book itself is published, or even finished, sometimes. Because Chris's book was originally conceived as a squirrel book, and also went through various changes of style, content and approach, before settling on the dragon element as dominant, it was a long and tricky job to get the covers right. The accompanying illustrations demonstrate what I mean. They are just a selection of roughs that were suggested, mulled over, and eventually rejected as being unsuitable for one reason or another.

Early attempts at covers

A different approach…

Over the rewrite period it also became obvious that a change of title was required. *Snigger and the Nutbeast* was hardly appropriate for a dragon book. A total rethink was called for. Various ideas were bandied about until someone at the publishers came up with the genius idea of using a dragon's eye. A very rough illustration of this was produced, approved as a concept, and an artist engaged to do justice to the outline suggestion. The artist concerned did more than that. He created an exceptional and iconic cover painting – which became the precursor for the whole of the series. That phenomenally talented artist is called Angelo Rinaldi. He very generously contributed the following information about his work for the books.

"Regarding the first cover, I was closely art directed and

given a fairly detailed brief to produce a close up of a pottery dragon's eye. This was before I had the luxury of the internet to do any referencing, so I went hunting in old bric-a-brac shops and found some green china figurines. I then took some inspiration from Chinese dragons, and worked up a pencil drawing which went through a few minor corrections regarding the shape of the eye and the teardrop. And then it was on to artwork, which is oil painted on canvas board to give the cover a distinctive textured look. The main challenge with the first set of covers in the series was making the dragon look like it was made of pottery, and alive! Of course by the time I came to do the later ones, I had the internet at my disposal for referencing. For example, The Fire Eternal benefited from some great reference of a Chinese golden dragon. The last piece of artwork for Rain and Fire was a departure from the series style, in that it was more

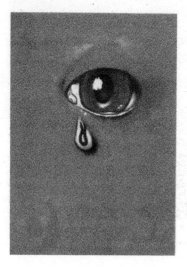

A breakthrough
idea at last

illustrative and less design led. I did several pencil sketches for this cover, in some the dragon looked more reptilian, in others too human, but I think we reached the right balance in the final piece."

An unused rough for Dark Fire

Although several titles were passed around for consideration, it was always Chris's intention to have the 'new' book called *The Fire Within*. For him, 'the fire within' represents the creative spark and, with the creation of Gadzooks as an externalised version of that, clearly that was what the book was all about. Chris was doing a school visit one day, and was explaining that *TFW* was a metaphor. Having established that the children knew what a metaphor was, he brightly asked if anyone would like to have a guess at 'a metaphor for what?'. There was a pause. Silence. Then one brave lad put his hand up and said, rather hesitantly, "Is it heartburn?" Chris no longer asks that question in his talks.

TFW was finally unleashed on the world in 2000. It did very well (and still does – it's in its 25th reprint), and was long-listed for the Carnegie Medal. Megan suggested that Chris do a sequel. He rather dozily replied that he could probably do two. Megan was delighted – a trilogy! And so it was that *The Last Dragon Chronicles* series was announced as such, erroneously as it turned out. Chris had no idea that there would be so much story to tell, and that it would eventually take seven books to do it.

8/1/05

Dear Chris

At a suitably snowy moment in London I've just finished reading Icefire!, which has been unputdownable from start to finish! It's absolutely spectacular. A real firecracker! The sweeping scope of the dragon legend is quite majestic, and the depth of thought and detail makes it compelling and utterly fascinating. It's a beautiful book, so obviously written from the heart that one cannot fail to be drawn into, and moved by, the depth of feeling and vision conveyed in the story. A triumph, Rain!

I just wish there was a bit more about Spikey! I think it must be because I'm missing the squirrels! And as for the Apple Tree (love it!) editor, the only similarity that struck me was the plate of Hobnobs on the desk — although the roadworks outside sounded all too familiar too! She does have a great line in encouraging rejection, young Dilys, that I think I might adopt myself...

Icefire is a real gem of a book. A jewel in your crown, that I'm immensely proud to have played a minuscule part in the creation of. Have fun with it. The cover's going to be a scorcher, and I can't wait to see the finished article.   Love Megan.

Usborne Publishing Ltd. Registered No. 1124359 England. VAT No. 240 8215 89 Bank: National Westminster Bank Plc, 1 Princes Street, London EC2R 8PA Account No. 00583700

A glowing report…

Real dragons

By this time, Chris was getting fan mail from all over the world, via his website. Over a hundred emails a week were arriving, from adults and children alike, all massively enthusiastic about the Pennykettle dragons, but many also wanting to know if a) there was going to be another book, and b) if so, could it have 'real' (i.e. large fire-breathing) dragons in it, as well, please. Interesting. 'As well', not 'instead of'.

Happy to oblige, off Chris went to do some research about 'big' dragons. At the library, he was ushered over to a bookshelf crammed to the ceiling with book upon book about dragons.

"All these?" Chris whimpered.

"And these. And those. And the ones over there," responded the librarian. Chris collapsed in a small heap (quite difficult when you're six foot two). Having been assisted back to his feet, he shambled out of the library and wandered off down the street, gibbering.

After that experience, he decided to simply make it all up. Thus a lady at one of his book-signing events, upon asking him how much research he did ("It must have taken you *years*..."), was rather taken aback when Chris said "none" and then promptly ran away to hide in the loo. It all seems to have worked out for the best, though – see Chapter 7 on 'Myths and Legends' to see if you agree.

The second book in the series, *Icefire*, was published two years later, and yes, the series does contain 'big' dragons from there onwards. Following the dragon eye cover concept, Angelo Rinaldi this time painted an ice-blue illustration, with an Arctic landscape reflected within the pupil of the dragon's eye. By the time the third book, *Fire Star*, came out (red, with a fire star within the eye), Chris's books were becoming a definite 'brand', being called the 'Fire' series by the fans, and even sometimes by the publishers. The fourth book, *The Fire Eternal*, was published (gold cover, the Earth in the eye), followed by *Dark Fire*, which has a very dark blue, almost black, cover, and a darkling (or 'anti-dragon') in the eye. It was at this point that the publishers wanted a 'proper' title for the series, and it officially became *The Last Dragon Chronicles*. And in fact, *Dark Fire* has the series title mentioned within its pages as part of the storyline.

Initially it seemed to be quite a task to find a definitive title for the series. It wasn't until Chris stopped and thought, *Whose story is this, really?* that it became apparent that it was not actually David Rain's, but Gawain's – the last known ('big') dragon in the world. Once that was established, it was simple.

There are over a hundred and twenty named characters in the first five books of *The Last Dragon Chronicles*. Human beings, squirrels and the little clay dragons made by Elizabeth Pennykettle dominate the first book in the series, *The Fire Within*. From there on the character base broadens out substantially and we meet polar bears, 'natural' dragons, alien life forms (both 'good' and 'evil'), and even Mother Earth. The following list focuses on those characters who play major roles in the series, even though some of them may appear only briefly, or in a single book.

The humans

DAVID RAIN: The hero of the books. He first appears as a young college student, when he becomes a lodger with the Pennykettle family. His curiosity about the clay dragons that Elizabeth (Liz) Pennykettle makes drives the whole series and fuels his increasingly dangerous investigations into the existence, history and mythology of dragons. As his journey progresses, we learn that there is a lot more to David than the innocent young man he first appears to be. In *Dark Fire* it is finally revealed that his connection to dragons runs very deep, and that his mission of discovery has been pre-planned by a greater intelligence called the Fain in an effort to prepare the Earth, and the human race, for a new era of dragon colonisation.

SOPHIE PRENTICE: David's first girlfriend. She appears towards the end of the first book, collecting charity envelopes for a local wildlife hospital. She helps David and Lucy Pennykettle look after Snigger and Conker, two squirrels who feature heavily in *The Fire Within*. Conker has an eye injury caused by a crow called Caractacus.

ELIZABETH (LIZ) PENNYKETTLE: The mother of Lucy Pennykettle, Liz lives at 42 Wayward Crescent, Scrubbley. Liz is a potter with a difference. She has the ability to make clay dragons which she can bring to life. Among the many dragons she makes in the series, the most important is probably Gadzooks, whom she makes as a house-warming gift for David. Liz is a distant but direct descendant of Guinevere, a woman who was with Gawain, the last known natural dragon in the world, when he died. Naturally, Liz has inherited her own 'dragonness' from Guinevere.

LUCY PENNYKETTLE: The feisty daughter of Liz Pennykettle. Lucy is just short of her eleventh birthday when David first comes into her life. She is sixteen by the time of the events of *Dark Fire*. She regards David as something of the 'big brother' that she never had. Her initial insistence that he help her save an injured squirrel leads to the discovery of David's ability to write stories (with the aid of Gadzooks). The books that David writes for Lucy (particularly a polar bear saga called *White Fire*) help to establish David as a cult author and indirectly draws Lucy into an edgy friendship with journalist Tam Farrell.

SUZANNA (ZANNA) MARTINDALE: The long-term girlfriend of David and later the mother of his daughter, Alexa. Zanna and David meet in *Icefire* when she is a sparky, gothic student. Her knowledge of all things 'new age' aids his investigations into dragon lore. Ultimately, it is revealed that Zanna is a sibyl, able to perform certain kinds of magicks. Although she loves David deeply, their relationship is often rocky and they clash frequently over Alexa's upbringing.

ARTHUR MERRIMAN: A brilliant physicist who is continually wrangling with the mysteries of the Universe and the power of human consciousness and creativity. He first meets Liz when he is a postgraduate student at Cambridge University and falls in love with her. Their relationship comes to a dramatic end when the sibyl, Gwilanna, tricks him into believing that Liz's love for him is not genuine. Distraught, Arthur joins a monastery and adopts the name 'Brother Vincent'. At the monastery, he finds a claw of Gawain and is empowered to write about David, little knowing that he is manipulating the so-called 'dark matter' of the Universe to create David's character. In *Fire Star*, he is reunited with Liz and thereafter lives with the family at Wayward Crescent.

GWILANNA: More of a nuisance than an out and out villain, Gwilanna is a sibyl and a kind of specialised 'midwife' who, like Guinevere, was around when the dragon Gawain died. Unlike Guinevere, Gwilanna has survived for thousands of years, keeping herself alive by the clever use of elixirs brewed from one of Gawain's scales. Arrogantly regarding herself as superior to any human, she constantly clashes with David. What saves her from his wrath on more than one occasion is her ancient knowledge of dragons and her role in the development of the descendants of Guinevere, e.g. Liz and Lucy Pennykettle.

ANDERS BERGSTROM: A mysterious and extremely influential character who first appears in *Icefire* as David's college tutor. He guides David in his investigations, teaching him about the connection between dragons and polar bears. Over the course of the series it transpires that Bergstrom was a polar scientist who vanished, in mysterious circumstances, on an Arctic exploration to the remote Hella Glacier. Thought to have been killed by a polar bear, Bergstrom has actually harmonised his life force with Thoran, the first polar bear ever to walk the Arctic ice. Bergstrom, in his role as an ambassador for raising awareness about the Arctic (particularly the dangers of global warming), is responsible for giving the young Liz Pennykettle (as a child) a snowball containing dragon 'auma', which she, now an adult, uses to animate her clay dragons.

HENRY BACON: A librarian who lives at 41 Wayward Crescent and a long-time, well-meaning but grumpy next-door neighbour to the Pennykettles. Although always on the periphery of the stories, Henry's significance grows when it is discovered that his grandfather was in the same party of explorers as Anders Bergstrom. In *Dark Fire*, Henry's collection of memorabilia connected with his grandfather's explorations provides direct evidence of the ancient existence of dragons.

TAM FARRELL: A journalist who first comes to prominence in *The Fire Eternal* when he tries to uncover the truth about David's background. His attempts to use Zanna to get information on David almost results in her killing him with magicks.

He makes amends when he rescues Lucy from the malevolent thought-beings, the Ix (an offshoot of the Fain) and thereafter becomes an ally to the family.

ALEXA MARTINDALE: Arguably the most important character in the whole series. Alexa is the charming five-year-old daughter of David and Zanna. Her abilities, which include telepathy with David and an apparent ability to predict the future, are largely ignored as a kind of advanced (but slightly expected) precociousness. Her importance comes to the fore in *Dark Fire*.

GUINEVERE: A young woman from the mists of time who held a passionate desire to see dragons survive. Although she is only ever mentioned as a character of legend, Guinevere's role in the story is hugely important, for she was present when the last known natural dragon, Gawain, died. She caught Gawain's fire tear, setting off a chain of events that is still continuing to the present day, via her descendants, Liz and Lucy Pennykettle.

The clay dragons

GADZOOKS: An inspirational writing dragon with a powerful ability to make events happen simply by writing down words on the notepad he carries. He guides David throughout the series and is influential in all the major developments of the story.

GROYNE: More bird-like than dragon and created for Anders Bergstrom by an Inuit shaman, not by Liz Pennykettle. Tremendously powerful, he can make himself invisible, morph into different shapes (particularly a small piece of narwhal tusk) and move whoever is carrying him through time and space.

GRETEL: A potions dragon who casts spells in the scents of flowers. Initially made for Gwilanna, she later defects to Zanna.

G'RETH: A dragon with the ability to grant wishes (but only if beneficial to dragonkind). He is the first point of contact with the thought-beings, the Fain (see page 62).

GOLLYGOSH GOLIGHTLY: A healing dragon made by David. 'Golly' can heal ailments, but is more often employed in fixing or solving mechanical or electrical problems.

GWENDOLEN: Specifically Lucy's special dragon and a whiz at IT. She comes to Lucy's rescue on many occasions.

GWILLAN: A kind and loving 'house' dragon who helps Liz with domestic duties and ultimately has a hugely significant role.

GRUFFEN: A slightly hopeless guard dragon, often involved on the periphery of dramatic events. Very young and new to the job, so he has to keep referring to his manual for the correct procedures to follow.

GRACE: A 'listening' dragon. She has the ability to pick up and beam signals from and to Liz, David, etc., or any of the other Pennykettle dragons.

GAUGE: A dragon with the unique ability to tell (and measure) time.

GLADE: Glade is a rarity – a Pennykettle dragon who lives with a 'normal' family (that of Lucy's friend, Melanie). Glade can detect and predict changes in mood. She enters the story in *Dark Fire*.

GAWAIN AND GUINEVERE: Two of Liz's clay dragons that rarely leave her pottery studio, the Dragons' Den. They have been named by her in tribute to their ancient namesakes. Their role is to 'kindle' other clay dragons into life. They are deeply mysterious and rarely mentioned.

THE LISTENER: Although a genuine Pennykettle dragon, he is never referred to by name for reasons that are not yet apparent. Like Grace, he has the ability to receive and send messages. He sits on the fridge top in the kitchen at Wayward Crescent.

The natural dragons

GAWAIN: He is the 'last dragon' the series title refers to. At the end of the last great age of dragons on the Earth, he was the final dragon to die. When he shed his 'fire tear' (documented in *Icefire*) he left behind him a legacy which fuels the whole series.

GROCKLE: A modern-day dragon born when Zanna

and Liz 'kindle' an egg between them. At the end of *Fire Star* he is taken by the Fain into their home world, Ki:mera, but returns to aid David in *Dark Fire*.

G'OREAL: A powerful ice dragon and the leader of the new 'Wearle' (or clan) which has been sent to recolonise the Earth.

The polar bears

THORAN: Originally a brown bear, he helps the woman Guinevere to escape from Gwilanna after Gawain, the last-known natural dragon, has shed his fire tear. In an extraordinary moment of magicks, he is turned into the first white bear to walk the polar ice cap and thereafter becomes a creature of legend.

LOREL: One of nine polar bears which ruled the ice at the time of Thoran. Lorel is a 'Teller of Ways'. His ability is to record, remember and recount all the legends of the Arctic.

RAGNAR: A fighting bear and another ruler of the ice. He is immortalised in legend when he sheds a tooth and beats it into the ice, apparently creating an island which comes to be known as The Tooth of Ragnar, though there is some debate as to the validity of this.

INGAVAR, AVREL, KAILAR: These three bears are the modern-day equivalent of Thoran, Lorel and Ragnar. The most important of them is Ingavar, who is present when David fights a dramatic battle with an agent of the Ix at the end of *Fire Star*.

Miscellaneous others

SNIGGER, CONKER: Two of many squirrels who used to live in Wayward Crescent. The tree where they used to drey was cut down, so the majority of them moved away. Conker gets left behind because he is injured. Snigger returns to assist in his capture, so that he can be examined by a wildlife vet.

CARACTACUS: A crow who injures Conker the squirrel when he gets too close to the crow's nest. Conker means no harm, but the crow is brutal in his defence of his young, who are about to hatch.

BONNINGTON: The Pennykettles' cat. He is transformed from a lazy, slightly stupid tabby into a 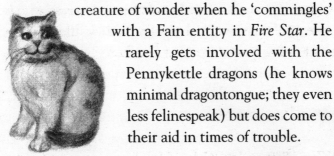 creature of wonder when he 'commingles' with a Fain entity in *Fire Star*. He rarely gets involved with the Pennykettle dragons (he knows minimal dragontongue; they even less felinespeak) but does come to their aid in times of trouble.

WINSTON: David's teddy bear. Does not have a large role to play, but he's there or thereabouts in the background.

BRONSON: A toy mammoth belonging to Alexa. She sends a thought projection of him to David in the Arctic at a crucial point in *The Fire Eternal*.

GAIA: The spirit of the Earth; Earth Mother. Appears in a variety of guises and semi-physical forms throughout the series. Helps Lucy, particularly in times of need.

THE FAIN: A mysterious race of beings who first enter the saga in *Fire Star* when G'reth, the wishing dragon, makes contact with one of them. The Fain have no physical body and exist in another dimension on a plane of thought, manipulating the dark energy of the Universe to create a thought-world known as Ki:mera around them (though this is never seen). The Fain can 'commingle' with any physical life form, but regard dragons as the most perfect form there is. The Fain's spiritual development depends upon them commingling with the 'white fire' of a living dragon, a process called 'illumination'. They frequently come to prominence as the story progresses, but their history with the human race is chequered, largely because humans and dragons have, in the past, struggled to live in harmony together on the Earth.

THE IX: Are, in effect, the flipside of the Fain. They are in a continuous unseen war with the Fain, seeking to gain control of the dark energy of the Universe to manipulate it for their own evil ends. In the past, they have attempted to use the imaginative power of humans to their advantage, leaving shadows of darkness in the human psyche (gargoyles, bogeymen, fear of spiders, etc.). Dragons are the physical enemy of the Ix, but the Ix have countered them by producing a template for an anti-dragon, a creature they call a darkling. Darklings are terrifying monsters, but are no match for dragons, because so far the Fain have been able to prevent the Ix from creating 'dark fire', the most destructive force in the Universe, which the Ix would need if they were ever to 'delumine' one of their darklings.

Character names

When Chris is asked to speak in schools, one of the questions he is always asked is 'where do you get the characters' names from?' He usually replies that they just pop up when they're needed. Although this is accurate, it's worth citing a few examples of how this happens.

A good place to start would be with David Rain, since he's the hero of the series. Chris was always fascinated by the stories he was taught about in his school RE lessons. He particularly enjoyed those about David (later King David) and they stood out in his memory. Thus 'David' comes from the Bible. 'Rain' is from a completely different source. Chris is a mad-keen Beatles fan and many years ago they released a double-A sided single with songs called 'Paperback Writer' and 'Rain'. Since Chris wanted to be the former, he thought his alter ego, David (who is based on Chris in his younger days), ought to be the latter. And while we're still on the subject of the Beatles, you might like to know that David's teddy bear is named after Chris's all-time hero, and the person Chris would have most liked to meet, John Lennon. Winston was John's middle name.

The Pennykettle surname is based on a previous neighbour of Chris's. As a boy he used to live next door to a family with the surname Kettle. Whether the lady of the house was called Penny or not, he can't remember.

Bonnington, the cat, comes from a road name close to our house in Leicester, even though Lucy claims, in *The Fire Within*, that he is named after Chris Bonington, the climber (who incidentally spells his version with a single 'n').

Mr Bacon is a serious nod to Mr Curry in the *Paddington* books, written by Michael Bond. Chris absolutely adores these. In fact, Paddington is his favourite children's character bar none.

Zanna was picked up on when he signed a book for someone of that name, as was Godith. The girl in question pronounced it *Go*dith, with the emphasis on the first syllable, but Chris changed the pronunciation to Go*dith* in the books. Either way, a superlative find.

Grockle, the modern-day natural dragon, is an onomatopoeic name, that is, he makes that sound when he tries (and fails) to produce fire.

Gadzooks couldn't have been called anything else. It's a magical name for a magical dragon. Besides which, he wrote it on his pad, so we couldn't mistake it.

The name Glade, another of the Pennykettle dragons, was suggested by a girl who emailed Chris. She just thought it would be a good choice, as it began with a 'g'. Chris thought so too, but had to wait a long time for her to make an appearance in the story. When she did, it was the perfect name for her, and again, couldn't have been anything else.

Lono, a mother polar bear, was 'pinched' from a chap who wrote a book about them, again as a tribute. It is his surname.

The listener, who sits on the fridge in the Pennykettles' kitchen, is the only dragon who isn't referred to by a name beginning with 'g' – or with any other letter. This mirrors Inspector Morse, the fictional detective, who was only ever known as Morse, until right at the very end of the run of television programmes. It was only then that the viewer learned his forename was 'Endeavour'. Will the listener's name be similarly revealed in due course? You'll have to read the seventh and last book in the series to find out...

In some cases Chris's characters have been based on the personalities of people he knows or has seen, rather than their names. For instance, Russ, the helicopter pilot for the Polar Research Station in Chamberlain, is loosely based on a working cowboy and musician that we know, who goes by the name of Austin Dan. And, believe it or not, Tam Farrell's entire dress sense is based on a chap featured on a fashion makeover show! Chris was so impressed with the jacket that the stylist provided this man with that he not only went out and bought an identical one for himself, but wrote it into the story. He still has it to this day.

Chapter 5: What's What – The Glossary

There are quite a lot of words in the series that are either obscure, in a foreign language, or simply made up by Chris. The following list should help you understand them all. Most are fully explained in the text as you come to them, so no need to think that you have to have a degree in languages and a memory the size of a planet to enjoy the books. You don't.

auma: is an **Inuit** word meaning 'fire'; Chris, however, uses it in *The Last Dragon Chronicles* to mean inner spirit or animating force, **the fire within**. Dragons are the animating spirit of the natural world. The more auma something has, the more lively or creative it is, and the closer to **Gaia** it becomes. Auma can be sensed, 'read', followed by someone sensitive to it, or raised, usually by specific intention and focus of thought.

bonglers: colloquial name for wind chimes with a relatively low note. As opposed to chinklers, those with a higher pitched or tinklier sound.

Ci:pherel: a **natural dragon** who can 'read' a person's auma and thereby detect whether they are telling the truth, or are who they claim to be.

coelacanthis: stasis; a state of suspended animation.

Cluster; Comm:Ix; Ix-risor: an **Ix** assassin, consisting of a few to a multitude of negative **Fain** entities.

commingle: to mingle or mix together. Used in the books to mean a conjoining of minds, or of whole personalities, usually involving an entity from a race of beings called **the Fain**.

Comm:Ix: see **Cluster**.

dark fire: the most destructive force in the Universe. Can be brought into being only by an **inversion** of a source of spiritual purity, such as a selfless act of love, or a moment of inspired creativity. A dragon born of dark fire would be a monster, known as a **darkling**.

darklings; semi-darklings: semi-darklings are potential anti-dragons, created and controlled by **the Ix**. They have no separate volition of their own. Attempts to **delumine** them, i.e. give them independent life via the introduction of **dark fire**, thereby making them into full darklings, have so far proved fruitless.

delumination: the means by which **semi-darklings** would be brought to independent life as full **darklings**, via the introduction of **dark fire**.

dream it: a phrase used predominantly by Liz Pennykettle to lull someone into a state of relaxation so they can 'live' what she is telling them, rather than just imagine it.

Fain, the: a race of thought-beings who have no physical body and exist in another dimension. They have the ability to **commingle** with any physical life form, the ideal being that of a dragon. This latter, highly desirable achievement, is called **illumination**.

fire eternal, the: another name for love, and as such, the title of a book of poems written by Tam Farrell. Also the spiritual fire (**white fire**) at the centre of the Earth, the source from which every **natural dragon** in this world springs. The greatest creative force in the Universe.

fire star: a 'portal' used by **the Fain** and **the Ix** to travel between their world and the Earth. It has been out of alignment with the Earth for a very long time, but is now coming into an appropriate position once again by the time of the third book.

fire tear: a single tear cried by a dragon immediately before it dies. All the fire that was within the creature is contained in this tear, which falls off its snout onto the ground. It then finds its way back to the fire at the centre of the Earth, from whence it originated. A dragon can be made to cry its fire tear before its due time by not loving it, or by otherwise making it extremely sad.

fire within, the: see **auma**.

fluenced: influenced, caused to do as intended by means of magicks.

fosh: Lucy's way of referring to fish. Taken from Allan Ahlberg's book *Ten in a Bed*.

Gaia, Gaia principle, Mother Earth: the principle that the Earth is a living and breathing entity in its own right, with needs, feelings, desires and intentions of its (her) own. She works in spirit form to keep the Earth in balance and has, in Chris's books, the ability to bring this about by appearing in many different guises, as circumstances demand, to those who can see her. As they help her, so she in turn helps them.

icefire: the substance with which Liz Pennykettle makes her clay dragons come to life. Given to her as a 'snowball' when she was a young child.

illumination: the result of the commingling of a Fain entity with a natural dragon. A highly desired spiritual goal and achievement.

i:lluminus; i:sola: the former is the illuminated being comprised of a **Fain** entity and a **natural dragon**, while they are **commingled**. The latter refers to the dragon element only of the pair, when the two are physically separated.

inua: soul, inner self.

Inuit; Inuk: native peoples of the Arctic regions, meaning 'the people'. Inuk is the singular form, meaning 'a man', 'a person'.

inversion: positive emotion such as love transformed into negative emotion such as fear, and used against enemies of **the Ix**, traditionally **the Fain** and their **natural dragons,** but now encompassing human beings also. **The Ix**'s intention is to induce humans into negative thought patterns and despair (such as believing there is no hope for the world to solve its problems of pollution, global warming, etc.), so that they can use these to power their semi-darklings, and ultimately to fuel a full darkling. Inner **white fire** turned into **dark fire.**

i:sola: see **i:lluminus.**

isoscele: the final triangular scale of a dragon's tail.

Ix, the: the negative element of **the Fain**; a breakaway group. They wish to gain control of the dark energy of the Universe, and are in the process of creating an anti-dragon called a **darkling**.

Ix:risor: see **Cluster**.

kabluna: white man; white person.

Ki:mera: the thought-world inhabited by **the Fain** and **the Ix** in a different dimension from the Earth.

mark of Oomara: a symbol of power which can be used for good or evil. The three jagged parallel lines of it represent the lives of men, bears and dragons – always running alongside each other, but never meeting. The mark, wherever it is found (on Zanna's arm; emblazoned on a polar bear's head, for example) brings an expansion of consciousness. Can be a blessing or a curse.

moyles: the final rows of teeth at the back of a **natural dragon**'s jaws.

mukluks: Arctic boots, made of skins, often trimmed with fur.

nanuk: polar bear.

nanukapik: literally 'greatest bear'. A leader from the ancient times when dynasties of bears ruled the ice, and lived in packs.

natural dragon: a 'real' dragon, large and fire-breathing, as opposed to Liz Pennykettle's clay dragons.

nauja: seagull.

Naunty, Nunky: colloquialised expressions of Aunty and Uncle, used by Lucy, and later by Alexa.

obsidian: a volcanic rock from which **the Ix** intend to create their **darklings**.

parthenogenesis: means of reproduction using only an unfertilised egg. How Liz and Lucy were created.

Premen: Early group of beings comprising of a **Fain** entity **commingled** with a human being. They ruled the Earth in those far-off days.

Prem:Ix: a human being permanently **commingled** with an **Ix** entity.

Pri:magon: a priestess. Gwilanna's mother was one such, mated to an uncommingled human male.

properly: normal definition of this word, but a note here to say that Lucy uses it grammatically incorrectly. This is deliberate, as part of her character.

puffler; snuffler; whuffler: descriptive terms for some of the Pennykettle dragons. Pufflers include Gloria, the dragon on the cistern in the loo who 'puffles' a nice rose scent in place of a more traditional type of air freshener. Snufflers include Gwillan, who as part of his household duties snuffles up dust (as an alternative to a vacuum cleaner), but would then puffle out the dust, as ash, later. Whufflers are responsible for the 'central heating', given that there are no radiators to be seen anywhere at number 42 Wayward Crescent.

qannialaaq: falling snow.

semi-darklings: see **darklings**.

sibyl: wise woman, prophetess, witch.

snuffler: see **puffler**.

stig: retractable thorn which decorates an adult **natural dragon**'s skeleton, particularly along the wings.

taliriktug: strong arm.

third eye: the pineal gland, alleged to be a channel of creative energy, the focus of extra senses ('sixth sense' and more) in humans and other beings.

tornak: a talisman of fortunes, the correct use of which enables insight into one's true path of destiny. In the books, this particular talisman is a piece of narwhal tusk, a variant form of a bird-like dragon called Groyne. Groyne can freely morph into different shapes, become invisible at will and travel through time and space, along with anyone who happens to be holding him at the time, when in his tornak form.

unnatural eye: an eye in which there is a deliberate defect in the duct, in every **natural dragon**. This is a kind of sac, a safety mechanism, in one eye only, that won't allow the whole **fire tear** to pass. A dragon shedding its tear in this way will always retain a little of its spark, and thus be enabled to hibernate for many thousands of years until the tear has fully regenerated.

Wearle: a dragon colony.

wearling: a young dragon belonging to and brought up in a dragon colony.

white fire: 'the fire that melts no ice'. The title of a book written by David Rain. Also see **the fire eternal**.

whuffler: see **puffler**.

wuzzled: sleepy or dazed.

wuzzled off: went to sleep, or a gentle euphemism for 'died', depending on the context. Usually used with regard to animals, but can be expanded to include humans.

Chapter 6: Where's Where – The Settings

Chris is often asked why, if *The Last Dragon Chronicles* series is a fantasy saga, most of it is set in the real world of day to day life, but where magical things happen. He has two answers to that. One is that the squirrel story at the heart of the first book, *The Fire Within*, is necessarily set in such a world, and so everything else had to be; the other is that he was initially very wary about creating something 'other', given his then rather poor track history of attempting to write science fiction stories. His confidence has grown considerably since, but the scene was set (or rather, the scenes were set) beyond any substantial change long before that point. Perhaps there is a third reason – that he simply thoroughly enjoys writing domestic-drama-type scenarios. It's what he relishes most of all.

Although there are many, many settings throughout the series, these can be largely separated out into three distinct groupings. Those in and around Scrubbley, where the Pennykettle family live; the Arctic icecap, and Ki:mera, the home thought-world of the Fain, which is never actually seen, so obviously cannot be described here.

Scrubbley

Scrubbley is, as already mentioned, a thinly-disguised Bromley, in Kent. Number 42 Wayward Crescent is an archetypal 1930s semi-detached house. Lucy's room faces the road at the front of the house. David's room is on the ground floor and faces onto the back garden, where much of the action featuring Henry Bacon, who lives in the property next door on the attached side, occurs. Most of the domestic scenes within the Pennykettle household centre round the kitchen and the Dragons' Den, the studio where Liz makes her clay creations:

All around the studio, arranged on tiers of wooden shelves, were dozens and dozens of handcrafted dragons. There were big dragons, little dragons, dragons curled up in peaceful slumber, baby dragons breaking out of their eggs, dragons in spectacles, dragons in pyjamas, dragons doing ballet; dragons everywhere. Only the window wall didn't have a rack. Over there, instead, stood a large old bench. A lamp was angled over it. There were brushes and tools and jam jars at the ready, plus lumps of clay beside a potter's wheel. The sweet smell of paint and methylated spirits hung in the air like a pot pourri aroma.

The scent of pot pourri also hangs in the air in Zanna's new age shop, The Healing Touch. She bought this property with the aid of royalties from David's two commercially successful books after he was lost in the Arctic, presumed dead. Liz helps her with childcare duties so that Zanna can work on building the shop up from scratch. The shop layout was inspired by that of a local health food store, though the latter is a bit smaller than Zanna's emporium, has neither an upstairs open to the public, nor a potions dragon to assist in making up the tinctures.

The previous owner had run the property as a small gift shop and had passed it on with all the fittings in place. Pine shelving racks occupied the two long walls and a glass display counter faced the door. Behind it, curtained off by bamboo strips, were two utility areas which served as stock room, preparation room and kitchen. The two rooms upstairs were as bare and dusty as Mother Hubbard's cupboard, but over the next three years, as her turnover increased and her reputation for producing effective 'lotions and potions' expanded, Zanna was able to decorate throughout and turn them into her consulting area, for clients requiring her unique brand of healing.

Tam Farrell, a journalist who is investigating David Rain's mysterious disappearance in the Arctic, buys a clay dragon from Zanna's shop one day, and invites her to attend a poetry reading at Allandale's bookshop in an attempt to win her trust and get her to open up to him with the truth. This book shop is based on one called

Browsers, which used to be situated in Allandale Road in Leicester but is sadly now closed; Sandra, who co-owned it, became Cassandra in the books.

...It was the same room, set out in just the same way, with three arcs of soft-backed chairs and a small lectern at the front. The main ceiling lights had been turned off, and the room was illuminated by filtered blue halogens built into the two walls of bookshelves. Ten or a dozen people were already randomly seated, poring over programme leaflets, but Zanna's eye was drawn to a larger group, clustered around a table where wine and fruit juice was being served. She spotted Tam Farrell in quiet conversation with a spiky-haired woman, whom she knew to be the book shop owner, Cassandra.

Zanna is distraught and very angry when she discovers that Tam is only befriending her because of his professional interest in David. However, when she is attacked by semi-darklings, on a place called North Walk, it is Tam who rescues her and thus becomes a trusted companion after all. In real life, North Walk is the image of a beautiful tree-lined avenue in Leicester called New Walk, which runs from the heart of the city to a lovely open park next to the University. It's exactly as described prior to the attack scenes, even including the museum and double-mouthed postbox – but minus semi-darklings and Tam Farrell.

New Walk in Leicester, the inspiration for North Walk

[North Walk] was a wide asphalt path that cut through the professional heart of Scrubbley. The Georgian town houses that ran along one side were mostly occupied by solicitors or accountants... Alexa preferred the other side of North Walk. There were houses and offices along here too, and a fine museum of art. But dotted between the buildings were squares and rectangles of urban grassland, shaded by vast horse chestnuts and oaks. Lucy had once written a story for school about two squirrels that lived on the edge of such a square. The name of the story was Bodger and Fuffle from 23 along. The number 23 referred to the broken glass lantern, on the twenty-third lamppost from the top end of the Walk, where the squirrels had built their drey. One of Alexa's favourite games was to count the lampposts aloud, even though she knew exactly which one

(by the double-mouthed red postbox just beyond the museum) was home to the legendary squirrels.

Not far from the park end of New Walk, Rutherford House (previously a lunatic asylum in the books), is based on a slightly adapted part of Leicester University's campus, which, incidentally, shared the same history before it became an educational establishment.

Although Caractacus the crow attacks Conker the squirrel in the garden at 42 Wayward Crescent in *The Last Dragon Chronicles*, the idea for this scene was implanted in Chris's mind many years before in the graveyard adjacent to another part of the University campus – the Medical School's car park. This is where Chris used to work for twenty-eight years before becoming a full-time writer. The Med School, not the car park, of course.

Conker's sanctuary

One day, he was called outside by a friend to witness (and try to capture) a grey squirrel running around in wide circles, obviously trying to escape from something but unable to move in a straight line. It transpired that a crow had made a lunge at it, for reasons unknown, and damaged one of its eyes. Despite a mad half-hour with Chris running around after it with an empty cardboard box, it did eventually manage to get itself away from both the crow and Chris, and finally disappeared under the fence and thence among the graves. Chris followed in hot pursuit, but never saw it again. The image and the memory stayed with him for over a decade before ultimately being written into literary history.

Beyond Scrubbley

A little further afield, the siting of The Old Grey Dragon guest house, where Lucy and Tam stay in *Dark Fire*, was based on a bed and breakfast that Chris and I stayed at in Glastonbury, right at the foot of the Tor. The owners were a wonderfully welcoming couple and absolutely nothing like the characters of Hannah and Clive, who own The Old Grey Dragon in the book. The back door of the guest house opened onto a private path that led onto the public one and thence right to the top of the Tor.

Once at the top of the Tor (called Glissington Tor in the novels), and with Tam's help, Lucy spies out the land with a view to raising a natural dragon that she believes has been in stasis for hundreds of years, somewhere beneath their feet. Opposite the Tor is another hill, Scuffenbury, where there is a chalk horse etched into the grass. It is alleged that when moonlight falls in a particular way on the horse's head, the dragon will awaken, but Hannah later suggests to Lucy that there is a better and easier way to achieve that – by touching the dragon itself. To this end, Hannah guides Tam and Lucy through some tunnels under the Tor which have been professionally excavated in years gone by, abandoned, then later extended by her husband.

In real life, the horse on Scuffenbury Hill is actually based on the white chalk horse at Uffington, in Oxfordshire. Glissington Tor itself, although based mainly upon Glastonbury Tor (especially for shape and size), is further influenced by the man-made mound at Silbury, Wiltshire. It is at this site that excavations were professionally made. Nothing unexpected was found there.

Further afield again, and in London now, both in the books and in real life, Apple Tree Publishing (the company which publishes David's books) is highly reminiscent of Orchard's (Chris's publishers') old offices...

The offices of Apple Tree Publishing were wedged between a builder's yard and a pub in a cramped and run-down area of London. It was hardly the castle of literary elegance that David Rain had imagined it to be. Redevelopment was everywhere. Half the road was chequered by scaffolding. Boards surrounded the knocked-out shop fronts. The smell of damp brick dust hung in the air. Black taxi cabs shuttled past, squirting slush onto the snow-packed pavements. And from every quarter there came a noise. Hammering, drilling, workmen shouting, music thumping out of the pub, the steady buzz of traffic, the rumble of a bus, the sucking whistle of an overhead plane.

...and the *National Endeavour* newspaper offices, where Tam Farrell works, of Orchard's new ones.

According to Gwendolen's place-finding search engine, the offices of the National Endeavour *were in a large building on Wellington High Road, half a mile's walk from the underground station of the same name. On her map, the thick green line of a major A road did not appear especially intimidating, but even though Lucy was no stranger to London, the pace of life here, in the rush hour, frightened her. Wellington High Road was a furious dual carriageway, yet there was traffic congestion on one side of the road, made worse by a fire engine and a clutch of police cars, which were throwing their blue lights into the rain... She pulled up her collar and hurried on past... By now, if her bearings were correct, she should be right on top of the magazine's offices. A lorry powered by, rattling every pane of glass in sight. Then a horn blared, making her squeal in fright, driving her towards a revolving door. She saw the word 'Endeavour' and just kept on moving, glad to let it carry her out of the noise.*

Incidentally, the character of Dilys Whutton, who appears in *Fire Star*, is an homage to one of Chris's previous editors, though he won't allow me to say which one! Probably scared he'll never be invited to 'do lunch' ever again.

He equally won't allow me to spill the beans about the location of Farlowe Island, for reasons that may or may not become clear in the fullness of time, according to him. Obviously keeping some little secret up his sleeve for a big 'reveal' later. Suffice it to say that it is a real island somewhere in the UK, it is shaped approximately like a cross with one bar longer than the other, and it is inhabited by monks. Though not by monks anything remotely like the ones of Chris's imagination...

David's home address, 4 Thousall Road, Blackburn, Lancashire, is based on another Beatles reference, from a song called 'A Day in the Life', which mentions something along the lines of there being four thousand holes in Blackburn, Lancashire.

Into the Arctic

The Arctic settings are much more generalised, and not often related to any specific real-life places. The one notable exception to this is Chamberlain, which is (*very* loosely) based on the existence of a town called Churchill in Manitoba, Canada. This is somewhere that Chris would love to visit, as for part of the year polar bears gather there in large numbers, waiting for the sea ice to freeze sufficiently so that they can go out to hunt seal, their staple diet. Whether he'll be welcome there after the inhabitants read his version of life in that neck of the woods is anybody's guess.

'Neck of the woods' isn't a particularly appropriate phrase to use, in truth, as 'woods' or even single trees are almost non-existent in that area because the weather conditions are not temperate enough for them to survive. Here's a passage from *Fire Star* that gives you a flavour of this remote Arctic setting.

[Zanna] dropped the parking brake and gunned the truck forward. Its rear wheels squealed as they bit the road. Snowflakes as large as lemons hit the screen and were quickly swept aside into a layer of slush. Zanna shifted her gaze to the east. Out towards open water, surrounded by dirt stacks and rusting junked machinery, lay the moody bulk of the grain elevator, a large white

ocean liner of a building, blackened with smoke from a nearby chimney, splashed against the bleak grey Manitoba sky. For eight months of the year, when the bay was clear of ice, Chamberlain fed the north with grain. The sight of it reminded her why they'd come. "Got your list?"

David unflapped a pocket...

...The romantic in him had wanted to see a bygone time of people in furs outside their igloos, chewing skins and dressing kayaks. But the latter-day reality wasn't even close. The 'igloos' were rows of painted wooden buildings, mostly squat residential cabins. The only suggestion of a native heritage was a parka-clad figure attending a dog team. The man had a cigarette hanging off his lip and two curtains of black hair sprouting shabbily from under his cap. The dogs, despite the unflagging cold, seemed as happy as a small herd of sheep in a summer field.

As they turned into the centre of town, David was reminded that one of the principal attractions of Chamberlain was its tourist industry. People came here to photograph bears. There were several gift shops testifying to it, plus an Inuit museum he'd heard Russ and Dr Bergstrom talk about. On its wall was a sign declaring, 'Five Citizens for Every Bear'. He took this to mean that the town's population was approximately one thousand, as he knew from his studies that somewhere around two hundred bears passed through Chamberlain annually. Yellow warning signs were everywhere, reminding people of it.

BE ALERT!
POLAR BEAR SEASON
October thru November
Memorise this number

The number in question was the polar bear 'police'. If any bad guys lumbered in, Chamberlain, it seemed, was ready to run them out of town.

Most of the other scenes are just out on the ice, nearer or further away from various real areas, though Chris has invented a village called Savalik, which is where Tootega, an Inuit worker at the Polar Research Station a few days' journey away, was born and brought up.

A modern settlement of twenty or thirty large wooden houses, [Savalik] mirrored Chamberlain in all but size. It was snowbound on three sides, the houses huddled in a cloistered heap like Christmas presents on a large white armchair. Tootega, when he saw it this time, was reminded of something David Rain had said about Inuit settlements looking like a room that you forgot to tidy. Anything an Inuk did not need, any broken-down appliance or unused item, he would cast away – but not very far. So it was in Savalik. An incongruous mix of brightly-painted roofs and overhanging wires and old oil barrels and junked bent metal and columns of steam. But it was home, and the dogs knew it, too. Their noses lifted at the first scent of seal meat warming in a pot. Their tails wagged. Their paws spent less time in contact with the ice. Orak, the lead dog, whose mapping was every bit as sensitive as his master's, was tugging his comrades towards the colony long before the whip was up.

Tootega has come to visit his grandfather, who is very ill, in his home in the settlement. Nauja, Tootega's sister-in-law, is looking after the old man.

Tootega went in, bowing his head. The old man, famed throughout the north as a healer and shaman, commanded great respect within the community and even more esteem at home. He gave a thin cry of joy to see his firstborn grandson and called out to Nauja, Mattak! Mattak! meaning she should bring them whale meat to chew. Tootega crossed the floor, surprised to find a woollen rug under his feet. It dismayed him every time he came to this house to see his grandfather a little more absorbed by southern culture. This room, with its wardrobes and lampshades and remote-controlled television was a painful affliction of the disease called progress. Tootega could readily remember a time when this proud and happy man, now lying in a bed that had drawers in the mattress and propped up loosely on a cluster of pillows, would have been surrounded by furs and harpoons and a seal oil lamp, with blood and blubber stains under his feet. On the wall above the bed, slightly tilted at an angle, was a framed embroidered picture saying, 'Home, Sweet Home' in the Inuit language. To see it made Tootega want to empty his gut.

Progress will always happen, in the High Arctic as well as everywhere else, of course. And this is not necessarily a bad thing. However, Chris is deeply concerned about the effects of pollution, global warming, climate change and so on, especially regarding polar bears, one of his favourite animals. So much so, that he has David, working at the research base already mentioned, write in a letter back home to Liz and Lucy:

'We spend our days analysing ice samples. Some of them date back hundreds of years. Zanna is checking for increases in toxic chemicals called PCBs, which can poison bears and other forms of wildlife, and I am melting ice cores down and making the tea – I mean making interesting graphs to monitor the levels of something called beryllium 10. This is to do with global warming. Dr Bergstrom thinks that changes in the levels of beryllium 10 coincide with an increase in sunspots or flares, which might be warming the Earth and making the polar ice cap melt. That's scary, especially for bears. Every year, the ice in Hudson Bay melts earlier but takes a little longer to refreeze. This means that bears are fasting more and more and will reach a point, maybe in the next fifty years, when they will not be able to survive their time ashore and will die of starvation out on the tundra. It's hard to believe that

the natural world we take so much for granted is constantly under threat from climatic change and that creatures like polar bears could so easily become extinct. So we are busy searching for long-term answers, feeding the data into our computers to try to predict how long the polar ice will last.'

So how can you and I make a difference? David writes *White Fire*, of course, to bring these issues to the attention of the public. But Chris feels that such a grand gesture may not be necessary. He believes (and has David and Tam Farrell believe, too) that a solution to global warming can be achieved with a single sentence. *Make polar bears an endangered species.* Tell this to the big industrial nations. If they approve it, they will be forced to protect the beasts' icy habitat, and in doing so, they might just save the world.

Chapter 7: Myths and Legends

One of Chris's few clear memories of his school days is being fascinated by the ancient stories of gods, kings and mere mortals as told by the Greeks and Romans. He has had a love for myth, legend and parable ever since. The opportunity to create a few of his own, therefore, was just too good to miss.

Instead of stories about flying too close to the sun or leaving threads through mazes, however, most of Chris's centre around polar bears and dragons – with a few sibyls thrown in for good measure. He did come across one genuine old Inuit tale along the way, and that is the story of Sedna, the sea goddess. Even then, he put his own twist on it, so it would be appropriate for inclusion in *The Last Dragon Chronicles*.

Sedna

The legend of Sedna was almost as old as the ice itself. Like ice, it had many variations, fashioned by slips of the tongue on the wind. But the version which came to the Teller of Ways* as he watched the sea goddess thrash her tail and squirm from her ocean home was this:

Sedna had been a beautiful, but very lazy woman. She had refused many offers for her hand in marriage,

*The 'Teller of Ways' is a polar bear who remembers and recounts the whole history of the Arctic as it applies to his kind.

preferring to sit around her father's igloo admiring herself reflected in the ocean. Her father was tired of this, as he was old (and therefore could no longer hunt) and starving.

One day, a hunter arrived and offered a trade: a kayak full of Arctic char – a kind of fish – in exchange for the man's daughter. Desperate, Sedna's father agreed.

The hunter, who had hidden his face in his hood all the time, arranged a place and date for the swap, and departed as mysteriously as he came.

That night, knowing he would not get his daughter's approval voluntarily, Sedna's father prepared a sleeping draught which he gave to her, telling her it was broth. She drank the brew, and fell into a prolonged deep sleep. Before she awakened, her father hauled her to the rendezvous, where the hunter was waiting with a kayak full of fish, as promised. As soon as the exchange had gone ahead, the hunter grew a pair of wings and flew off with Sedna. As if that wasn't enough, the fish were rotten, too.

When Sedna woke and realised what had happened, she was terrified to find that her new husband was actually a raven – the king of ravens, in fact. She howled out her fear, which was taken by the north wind to the ears of her father, who was wracked with sadness and guilt.

He therefore set out in his old patched kayak to

rescue her, which he managed to do – to a point. However, before they could get away completely, they were spotted by Sedna's husband, who came after them to get his wife back.

Sedna's father hadn't enough strength to paddle their boat any faster, so it was not long before the raven caught up with them. The bird dived at them, scaring the father into offering Sedna back to him. Sedna, at first disbelieving of her father's treacherous act, soon changed her opinion when he pushed her over the side of the kayak. The water being bitterly cold, Sedna could not help herself back into the boat, and could barely even grip the side of it to keep afloat. Her father, by now addled with terror, for the raven was attacking ferociously, grabbed the kayak paddle and began to pound Sedna's fingers with it.

She wailed in agony but he would not stop. "Take her! Take her!" he shouted crazily, believing that the only way to save his life was to sacrifice his daughter's life instead. Over and over again he struck, until one by one, her frozen fingers cracked. They dropped into the ocean where they turned into seals and small whales as they sank. With her hands broken, Sedna could not hold on to the boat. Her mutilated body slipped under the water and slowly faded out of sight…

Yet, she did not perish. Poisoned by the magic of a raven's bile and further tormented by unresolved grief, she made her house at the bottom of the sea, where she became the goddess of the ocean, raging at men through violent storms...

If you want to know why David Rain calls the now terrifying, rather than terrified, Sedna up from her home at the bottom of the ocean, and what he has to offer her to get her aid, you'll have to read the book! In this instance, *The Fire Eternal*, the fourth in the series.

Chris's myths and legends

The following pages relate several snippets from some of Chris's own myths and legends, but so your enjoyment of the books won't be spoiled, I won't tell you the endings. Sorry! An extract from Lucy's journal would be a good place to start.

My name is Lucy. Lucy Pennykettle. I'm sixteen. I turn heads. I get noticed. A lot. Mainly for the bright green eyes and mass of red hair. I live in a leafy little town called Scrubbley with my mum, Liz, and her partner, Arthur, and my part-sister Zanna, and her sweet kiddie, Alexa. My cat, Bonnington, is the weirdest dude in fur you'll ever meet. We share the house with a bunch of special dragons, like the one sitting next to my keyboard, Gwendolen. Dragons. More about them in a mo.

Arthur (wise stepdad, sort of) told me once that people believe what they see in print. So here are a few small truths about me, just to get things into perspective:

My favourite food is vanilla-flavoured yoghurt. I'm slightly scared of moths. Squirrels break my heart. I think I'm in love with a guy called Tam. I'm totally in awe of the author, David Rain. I'm worried about the mist that's covering the Arctic. I'm haunted by the shadow of beings called the Ix. But there's one thing that keeps me awake most nights, and lately I can't wrap my head around it: I look like a girl. I walk and talk and act like a girl. But I was not born the way other girls are. I hatched – from an egg.

I AM NOT HUMAN

One of the *special* dragons, Gadzooks, eventually goes to visit a chap called Professor Steiner and writes something on one of the prof's parchments:

He crossed over to his desk and unlocked a drawer. From it he withdrew a single sheet of paper. It appeared to be made of thick grey cotton, like a small hand towel stiffened with starch. He passed it first to Lucy, who glanced at the pen marks and said, with disappointment, "It looks like a doodle."

[Elizabeth] took the paper and examined it. "I see what Lucy means. There doesn't appear to be a formal phonetic

structure. Though the strokes suggest it. They're very deliberate."

"I agree," said Rupert Steiner, buoyed by her assessment, "but it's quite unlike anything I've interpreted before."...

..."Just a moment, Professor." Liz cut him off and turned her attention to Gwendolen, who'd just given out a startled hurr. The little dragon was on the coffee table, standing by the sheet of paper.

"What's the matter?" Liz asked her.

The professor steered his gaze between the dragon and the woman. "Goodness! Can you converse with it?"

"Yes," said Liz, without looking up. "Go on, Gwendolen."

Gwendolen stepped forward and pointed to the writing. I know how to read it, she hurred.

"How?" said Lucy.

"It's dragontongue," Gwendolen said (rather proudly).

Lucy moved her aside. "Dragontongue? I didn't even know you could write it down."

"Nor me," Liz admitted, sitting back, stunned. [She] glanced at the writing again. "Gwendolen has just explained that the curves on the paper are like the way she moves her throat to make growling sounds."

"Yeah, but what does it say?" pressed Lucy.

Gwendolen gathered her eye ridges together and frowned at the markings again. It was not a word she recognised, she said, but she thought she could speak the pronunciation correctly. She cleared her throat and uttered a long, low hurr.

Lucy glanced at her mother, who gave the translation. "Scuffenbury," said Liz.

Scuffenbury in dragontongue

After a chat with David, Lucy now thinks she knows a bit more about why Gadzooks wrote 'Scuffenbury' on Professor Steiner's parchment:

At the end of the last dragon era, it came to a point where there were just twelve dragons left. Driven from their eyries by wild-hearted men who knew no better than to kill a creature they couldn't tolerate and didn't understand, the dragons came together and decided to surrender. They didn't give themselves up for capture or sacrifice; they just refused to fight any more. This, to me, is the saddest story ever. I grow tired of people who only think of dragons as fire-breathing, maiden-snatching, cave-dwelling monsters. Dragons had heart. Morals. Courage. Zanna always says they were the spiritual guardians of the Earth, and for once I agree with her. We don't really know what happened to the twelve. The legend is they separated and flew away to isolated places, remote volcanic islands and the like, where they could live out their lives in peace, and where they could eventually die in peace. Up until yesterday, the only location I knew about was the Tooth of Ragnar, where Gawain set down. Now, if David is telling the truth, there's one hidden underneath Glissington Tor, near to Scuffenbury Hill, not a million miles from here

Professor Steiner has also informed Liz and Lucy that he has seen dragontongue written before – in some photographs of wall markings taken in caves at a place called the Hella glacier. Henry Bacon, the Pennykettles' next-door neighbour, tells David of an incident that happened there when Henry's grandfather was part of an expedition to explore the area, in 1913. A fellow explorer had disappeared there in unusual circumstances – lost, presumed dead. Lorel is a polar bear captured in a photograph on the study wall.

"*People say he wandered off to find his watch.*"

"What?"

"*Had a dodgy incident a few months before. Found himself stranded near a native settlement with a large male polar bear for company. No rifle, and too far away from camp to summon help. All he had about him was a pocket watch. Played a tune when you opened the case. Our chap set it down in front of the bear. Story goes the bear swaggered up to the watch, sat down, watch betwixt paws, and listened. Our chappie backed off and escaped to camp. Went back with his comrades twenty minutes later, but the watch and the bear had both disappeared.*"

"*Who was this man?*" *David asked nervously.*

[Henry] pointed to a [photographic] plate at the bottom of a page. "*Third from the left. Fair-haired. Scandinavian.*"

David cast his eyes down.

It was Dr Bergstrom…

…David's mind wrestled with the impossible conundrum

of how a man in his forties, who lectured at Scrubbley College, could look exactly like a polar explorer reported missing in 1913.

David thought about Lorel and turned to look at the bear print again. For a fleeting moment he became the bear, looking back into the lens of Bergstrom's camera. And from somewhere between the bear and the man, from the bright cold wilderness of frozen ages, from the leaves of books, from the creaking timbers of ice-bound vessels, came a voice like a wind from another world saying, There was a time when the ice was ruled by nine bears...

There was a time when the ice was ruled by nine bears...

(…which is a whole other story: Chris's own massive *White Fire* Arctic saga. But you can read a little more about the nine in *Icefire*.)

And finally, I can't close this section without bowing to the wishes of a huge number of fans who have begged to know why all the dragons' names begin with a 'G'. The answer is in *Dark Fire*, but for those of you who haven't read that far yet, here goes. A little preamble from Arthur first, then the reveal by Gwilanna (she's got to be good for something). By the way, an isoscele is the last triangular scale of a dragon's tail.

"When I was at the abbey, I had a dream. I saw the universe created from the outgoing breath of a dragon called Godith. Everything was born from the fire of that dragon. A white fire. Auma in its purest sense. You and I, this physical world we inhabit, came into being when the fire cooled down to a low enough vibration to produce ingenious combinations of atoms and molecules."

Hy-dragon, rather then hydrogen, one assumes. Well, we humans nearly got it right!

"The letter 'G'," said Zanna.

"Not just any 'G'," Gwilanna drawled on. "A 'G' curling into an isoscele. It represents the tail of their creator, the she-dragon, Godith. Haven't you ever wondered why

102

dragons copy it into their names? To have the sign of Godith on your breath is a mark of respect. Really, girl, you're such a waste. You could have learned so much from me."

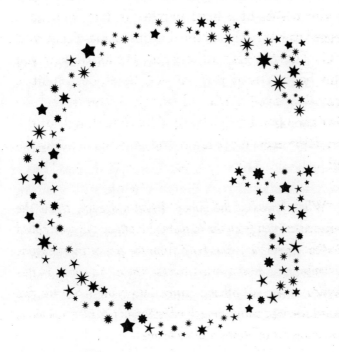

So now you know.

Chapter 8: The Light and the Dark

The first book in the series, *The Fire Within*, is an apparently simple, straightforward and charming story about a young man who comes to stay as a lodger with a single-parent family, helps rescue an injured squirrel, and makes the acquaintance of a few clay dragons along the way.

Even if it was that simple, it gives absolutely no clue as to the power and profundity yet to come in the rest of the books. The stories get deeper, darker and much more complex as they progress, while still retaining their trademark humour – from slapstick to black comedy – even in the direst of circumstances.

The storylines range from cosiest domestic drama to an interdimensional war between races of thought-beings, into which humans are in danger of being dragged. There is mystery, danger and adventure by the bucket-load, and this chapter gives a glimpse of what happens in each.

The Fire Within

The series starts with David Rain about to move into the Pennykettle household in Wayward Crescent. David is marvelling at one of the small clay dragons he has seen all around the house ever since he first walked in the door of Liz and Lucy's home. He does not yet know that they can come to life.

There was a fiery pride in its oval-shaped eyes as if it had a sense of its own importance and knew it had a definite place in the world. Its tall slim body was painted green with turquoise hints at the edges of its scales. It was sitting erect on two flat feet and an arrow-shaped tail that swung back on itself in a single loop. Four ridged wings (two large, two small) fanned out from its back and shoulders. A set of spiky, flag-like scales ran the entire length of its spine.

David picked it up – and very nearly dropped it. "It's warm," he said, blinking in surprise.

"That's because—"

"It's been standing in the sun too long," said Mrs Pennykettle, quickly cutting her daughter off. She lifted the dragon out of David's hands and rested it gently back on the shelf.

David soon learns that Liz Pennykettle makes these dragons, styled in a variety of poses and often with certain characteristics emphasised. She sells some of them at the market in Scrubbley. Liz has a studio in a room upstairs, called the Dragons' Den, and the new lodger is told in no uncertain terms by Lucy that he is not allowed to enter. Needless to say, this piques

David's curiosity, but he manages to stifle the impulse to have a sneaky look in, at least for a while.

In the meantime, Lucy, who is very fond of wildlife, implores David to help her to find an injured squirrel she has seen in the garden, and which she has named Conker. David agrees after some cajoling, but upon meeting the Pennykettles' next-door neighbour, Henry Bacon, he realises that he will have competition for this task. Henry's interest in capturing the squirrel is not benevolent, as he believes that squirrels have been responsible for eating his flowers and digging up his bulbs. To this end, he has got the local council to chop down a grand old oak tree that used to be home to a whole group of these creatures, which have now disappeared from the area. Only Conker is left behind.

Back in the Dragons' Den, Liz has been making a 'special' dragon for David, as a house-warming gift. Despite Lucy's dire warning for him to stay out of the studio, Mrs Pennykettle invites him in, where he gets introduced to several of the small dragons who are resident in the household. David's dragon turns out to be similar to the other dragons, except that it (he) is holding something…

…It had a pencil wrapped in its claws and was biting the end of it, lost in thought.

"Hope you like him," said Liz. He was…interesting to do."

"He's wonderful," said David. "Why's he got a pencil?"

"And a pad?" said Lucy, pointing to a notepad in the dragon's other paw.

"It's what he wanted," said Liz, coming to join them. "I tried him with a book, but he just wouldn't have it. He definitely wanted a pencil to chew on."

"Perhaps he's a drawing dragon," said Lucy. "Do you like doing pictures?"

David shook his head. "Can't draw for toffee. How do you mean, he 'wanted' a pencil?"

Liz lifted a shoulder. "Special dragons are like characters in a book; I have to go where they want to take me."

Lucy let out an excited gasp. "You mean he's a dragon for making up stories?!"

"Lucy, don't start," said Liz. "Now, David, if you accept this dragon you must promise to care for him always."

"You mustn't not ever make him cry," said Lucy, as if it ought to be obvious.

"Imagine there's a spark inside him," said Liz.

"If you love him, it will always stay lit," beamed Lucy.

"To light it, you must give him a name," said Liz.

"Something magic," said Lucy. "Think of one – now!"

David had a think. "How about…Gadzooks?"

Now that Lucy knows Gadzooks is a writing dragon, she asks David to make up a story for her about how Conker damaged his eye. Initially, David refuses. But later, with Gadzooks' help, he begins a tale about Conker and another squirrel called Snigger, as a present for Lucy on her birthday. This story turns out to be not only a recounting of events that have already occurred, but also a prophetic scribing of the near future. Whatever David writes about, happens.

In due course, David and Lucy do manage to catch both Conker and Snigger (the latter accidentally). Along with Liz, they take the two squirrels to the vet at a local wildlife hospital, where David's girlfriend, Sophie, works. Snigger is given a clean bill of health, but Conker is not so fortunate. He is given only a short time to live. Hoping to give the dying animal a last few happy days, the group release the squirrels in the library gardens. David manages to finish his story for Lucy, but the ending is very rushed and unsatisfactory. David is trying to give it a positive outcome, but becomes frustrated and ignores Gadzooks when this seems impossible. Gadzooks becomes very unhappy, to the point where he is in danger of crying his fire tear.

A fire tear is something that a dragon cries at the end of its life. Inside it is all the fire that was within the dragon throughout its existence. This tear then falls off the dragon's snout, drops onto the ground and finds its way back to the fire at the centre of the Earth, from whence it originally came. The only exception to this is related in a legend that runs through *The Fire Within*. This legend concerns Gawain, the last known real (or 'natural') dragon in the world, and after whom one of Lucy's 'special' dragons is named.

David yawned and snuggled into his pillow... His body relaxed. His mind drifted. He saw Gawain on a mountain top, silhouetted against the shimmering moon; Guinevere, wrapped in a kind of shawl, singing into the shell of his ear. Gradually, the dragon lowered his head. His spiked tail drooped. His scales fell flat. His oval eyes, long-closed and weary, blinked one final, fiery time. His life expired in a snort of vapour. But in that moment a teardrop formed. A living teardrop, on his snout. A violet flame in a dot of water. It trickled down his face to the tip of his nostrils and fell, sparkling, into Guinevere's hands.

But could she survive the power of the dragon's auma? And can David correspondingly save Gadzooks from shedding his own fire tear? What happens when David rewrites the end of Lucy's story? And what has Spikey, the hedgehog, got to do with it all? Well, some things are best revealed by reading the book...

Icefire

The second book in *The Last Dragon Chronicles* series opens with David receiving the latest in a long line of rejection letters from various publishers. He has been trying repeatedly to get his squirrel story accepted, but with no success so far.

By now, David has discovered that, as a child, Liz was given a mysterious snowball, a pinch of which enables her to bring her clay dragons to life. He is keen to find out the secret of this 'icefire', which he knows is guarded by polar bears in the frozen north. When the enigmatic Professor Bergstrom, a visiting lecturer at college, tells him about a competition to win a field trip to the High Arctic in Canada, David is desperate to win it. The rules, though, are rather unusual. He must write an essay as to whether dragons ever existed on the Earth. David decides to ask Liz for information. At the same time, he begins writing a second book, *White Fire*, about the Arctic and polar bears.

David gets further help for his essay from a goth girl called Zanna, who is on the same course as him. She offers to lend him a book on dragons. As his girlfriend, Sophie, is now away working in Africa for eight months, David feels somewhat awkward about inviting Zanna to Wayward Crescent, especially as Liz and Lucy have gone out that afternoon. Nevertheless, he shows Zanna the Dragons' Den. While there, she spies a wishing dragon, G'reth, made by Lucy, and a bronze clay egg. Zanna persuades David to make a wish.

David screwed up his face. "I'm not playing wishing games."
"It's not a game, dummy. You're raising his auma.

Believe. *Wish for something – about Gawain.*"

"*Such as?*"

"*Such as finding out where his* fire tear *is hidden?*"...

...*David sighed and looked away. This is ridiculous, he told himself. It won't work. It can't work. A wishing dragon? It was the stuff of fairy tales. But knowing he'd get no peace until he tried, he touched his thumbs to G'reth's smooth paws.*

"*Careful,*" *whispered Zanna,* "*you're making him wobble.*"

David steadied his hands and tried again. "I wish," he drawled, "that I knew the secret of Gawain's fire tear."

Zanna, meanwhile, who feels oddly drawn to the clay egg, somehow manages to 'kindle' or 'awaken' it. These two actions result in an immediate response from the Universe.

An evil sibyl called Gwilanna turns up, calling herself 'Aunty Gwyneth'. She claims to be a relation of Liz and Lucy's. She demands to see Liz, who arrives almost at the same moment. Gwilanna has been 'called' by the wisher, and is surprised to detect a powerful auma change in Liz, denoting that she is the equivalent of 'pregnant' (eggnant?) because of the kindling of the bronze egg by Zanna.

In theory this pregnancy should not be possible. Gwilanna believes that Liz's auma is getting stronger, whereas, with all the other descendants of Guinevere

111

(for that is what Liz and Lucy are) it is getting weaker, generation by generation, as expected. This causes 'Aunty Gwyneth' to question why this might be so. Getting no response from either Liz or Lucy on the subject, she determines to interrogate the wishing dragon instead. Gwilanna demands help from Gretel, another Pennykettle dragon, who belongs to her and is under her power.

G'reth gulped and swallowed a plug of smoke. Under normal circumstances, this would not have caused any problems for him. But the fact that he was hanging upside down, tail knotted round a thin wire coat hanger, which in turn was hooked around the light bulb holder swinging precariously left and right, had brought on a dreadful bout of coughing, which only added to his predicament – and his fear.

Aunty Gwyneth clicked her fingers.

Gretel, sitting on the corner of the wardrobe, opened her throat and released a jet of fire. There was a smell of burning and the green earth wire in the core of the light flex sizzled red-hot and duly snapped. The flex lurched, jerking G'reth another millimetre or two towards the mass of rubble littering the floorboards. Though his wings were bound (by Aunty Gwyneth's industrial strength hair pins) he nevertheless managed to swing his head upwards. All that remained of the light flex now was a strand from the outer sheath of white and the light-blue neutral wire. With a

112

whimpering hrrr? *he looked towards Gretel. She blew a tart wisp of smoke and looked away…*

Getting no useful information from G'reth, Gwilanna decides to take a sneakier approach and aid David in his quest to get to the Arctic, hoping that he will discover more on her behalf. To this end she 'fluences' an editor to not only accept David's squirrel book, but also to publish his polar bear saga. Zanna wins the essay competition, but David can now afford to pay his own way for the field trip, using the money due to him for writing his books.

But what of Liz and the egg?

Liz is semi-comatose while the egg is going through the hatching process. The 'boy' that Liz has been told to expect turns out to be a male dragon, the first 'natural' dragon to be born in modern times. Zanna reaches out to touch it, and is scarred by Gwilanna's fingernails with three jagged lines which never heal. Under cover of this distraction, the dragon escapes through the open window and, aided by G'reth, flies to Bergstrom's rooms. David, having overcome Gwilanna, follows with Zanna and Gretel. Gretel, by now, has swapped her loyalties to become Zanna's dragon.

At Rutherford House, where Bergstrom lives, Zanna discovers that the young natural dragon, whom she calls Grockle, has been born without fire. She is upset by this, even more so when he turns to stone in her arms, and totally distraught when she finds out that David suspected this might happen, but failed to warn her.

Zanna disappears, refusing to speak to David. Although he tries to find her, he has no luck. The days pass and eventually, just before David is due to go to the Arctic, the contract from the publishers arrives.

"Sign," Lucy urged him.

But Liz raised a hand. "Wait. Have you read through this properly?"

"Sort of. It's just...legalities and stuff."

"Exactly. You ought to know what you're signing. Perhaps Henry could check it for you?"

"It's all right," said David. "It's just boring blurb. Don't spoil my big moment. Pen, someone?"

Lucy grabbed one off the worktop and handed it over.

"Signed... David... Rain," David muttered, scratching his name on the line marked 'author'.

David has no time to do anything further – his lift to the airport is about to arrive and he therefore asks Liz for a favour.

"I need to post David's contract for him." Liz picked it up off the kitchen table. For a moment she stood there reading a chunk, then she began to quickly flick through it. At the

final page, she stopped and stared. "Lucy, you know that pen, the one David used to sign his name. Does it leak?"

Lucy drew a few lines with it, on her hand. "A bit, yes."

"As much as that?" Liz turned the page around.

From the lower curves of David's signature, three long trails of ink had formed.

Lucy tilted her head...and shuddered. "They look like Zanna's scratch..."

Was Lucy right to shudder? What effect will these lines called 'the mark of Oomara' have on Zanna and on David? Will David find the secret of Gawain's fire tear, as he wished? And if so, will he live to regret it?

Fire Star

David makes it to the field trip, with Zanna by his side again, and continues writing his book. Things are beginning to get more and more complex and confusing for him, though, as he realises that once again, his writing is mirroring real life. This leads him into questioning his beliefs about the world and his role in it, especially when something called a fire star becomes more and more apparent in the sky, and this portal is due to open a way between worlds.

David has been writing that Gwilanna is determined to raise the natural dragon, Gawain, from a mountain top on an island in the Arctic called the Tooth of Ragnar. This mountain is where Gawain cried his fire tear and turned to stone in ages past. Guinevere, the woman who caught his tear, had allegedly agreed to trade it with Gwilanna for a daughter. However, the trade never took place.

The child, Gwendolen, was brought up by Gwilanna, but eventually turned her back on the sibyl and went to live among the bears, earning their love and respect. Gwilanna has always hated the bears for this, and is therefore prepared to use them selfishly for her own devious ends.

David writes that Gwilanna has promised to heal a bear called Ingavar, who has been shot, if he will retrieve a polar bear tooth for her. David carries this talisman round his neck on a cord. Gwilanna tells Ingavar to kill him when he has succeeded.

David's story finally comes to a head when he and Zanna are faced by Ingavar at a trading post in Chamberlain. Fortunately, Ingavar is tranquillised and taken away to polar bear 'prison'. The tooth, however, is lost in the melée, but is picked up by Tootega, the Inuit guide who works at the research base where David and Zanna are staying.

Zanna, by now aware that David has the power to write 'fact' rather than simply fiction, is none too happy about this state of affairs.

*

"This is just too spooky," said Zanna. "Read the story, Dr Bergstrom. Now."

Bergstrom glanced at the open laptop, weaving coloured pipe work on its flat grey screen.

"No, I'm destroying it," David said. He stepped forward and moved the mouse. Bergstrom immediately clamped his arm...

..."I'm wiping it." And he dragged the file into the computer's trash can and emptied it.

This was still not enough for Zanna. "Defrag the disk."

"What?"

"I don't want it in memory, even in bits. Run a defrag over it. Now."

"But—"

"Just do it, David."

"Be my guest," said Bergstrom, wheeling his chair away.

Silently furious, David ran the program that would rearrange the disk so that all the files were contiguous and any scraps of deleted files were eliminated. "There. Happy now?"

Unbeknown to David, however, Bergstrom has previously printed out a copy – but to what purpose? Anders Bergstrom is definitely not what he first appeared to be. A lecturer, yes, but much, much more than that, for not many lecturers can shape-shift between man and polar bear... Or possess a small dragon not unlike those that Liz makes, who can travel through space and time, also shape-shift, and become invisible to boot...

Meanwhile, back in Wayward Crescent, Gwilanna has abducted Lucy to be a 'Guinevere clone' to aid in the raising of Gawain. Lucy has been taken to a cave on the Tooth of Ragnar, where she is to be held for the next three months, until the fire star is in its correct alignment. While there, she finds an isoscele, the last scale of a dragon's tail, belonging to Gawain, which she hides from Gwilanna.

After a frantic phone call from Liz, informing him of Lucy's fate, David returns home early from the Arctic. Zanna remains behind and, with Tootega, helps release the tranquillised polar bear back onto the ice. Gwilanna, in raven form, creates a blizzard, hoping to steal the tooth at last, but her plans backfire when three polar bears arrive and carry Zanna off with them.

While all this is happening, G'reth, the wishing dragon, is still trying to fulfil his duty and find the whereabouts of Gawain's fire tear for David. Rather like David, his investigations are about to take him far beyond what he might have expected. He manages to travel outside the boundaries of the known Universe and there meets up with a young entity from a race called the Fain.

[G'reth] had a startling impression of emptiness now. No light. No colour. No temperature. No smell. And yet he sensed he was not alone.

He was not.

He felt it enter through the tip of his tail, lift the scales along his spine and whisper through the tunnels of his spiky ears. Intelligence, finding its level, like water. A youthful, happy being, fusing with his auma.

What are you? it said, tickling his thoughts.

What are you? G'reth asked it.

I am Fain, it said. Shall we commingle?

The Fain are thought-beings, who have no physical form of their own, but can merge or 'commingle' with any other entity, sharing their host's body. They have a long and benevolent historical connection with dragons, and their ultimate aspiration is to merge with one. G'reth is transformed by this experience, returning back to the known Universe along with the young Fain.

By the time G'reth gets home, Liz has taken Bonnington, the Pennykettles' cat, to the vet. It is not good news. Bonnington is dying. His plight does not appear to be helped by drinking some melted icefire water. There is one beneficial outcome from this sad news, however. Grockle, the young natural dragon who turned to stone at the end of *Icefire*, has been brought back to the Dragons' Den, where he rests in a basket of straw. With the aid of the young Fain being and a drop of Bonnington's saliva, the Pennykettle dragons bring Grockle back to full life. Once again, Grockle escapes through an open window.

David asks Gadzooks for help to find Grockle.

[Gadzooks] scribbled something fiercely across the pad. Gretel and G'reth leaned in to take a look, exchanging a puzzled hrrr at what they saw. David closed his eyes to picture the message. It surprised him too. A name:

ARTHUR

He whispered it aloud.

As usual, he had no idea what it meant (at first). Insight would come a little later, from Liz. Right then, however, she was incapable of speech.

She had just fainted in a heap on the floor.

David discovers that Arthur is the love of Liz's life. Many years earlier, he was tricked by Gwilanna into breaking off the relationship and has had no contact with Liz since. Eventually David traces Arthur to a place called Farlowe Island, where he has become a monk, changing his name to Brother Vincent. Arthur has also been writing fact as fiction, using a claw belonging to Gawain as a pen. Grockle, seeking the claw, has been drawn to the island and hidden there by Arthur. Arthur's secret is given away to the abbot by one of the other monks, Brother Bernard, who later regrets his actions, as Grockle is captured, held in a stable block, and tortured.

Grockle in chains

Bernard, realising that what Arthur has told him is the plain truth and that the dragon is sentient and capable of communicating with him, asks:

"*Where did you come from?*"

The dragon raked the ground. It seemed to understand, but its answer was vague and made no sense.

Zannnnnaaaa, *it growled.*

"*Zannnnnaaaa? What is Zannnnnaaaa?*" *Bernard said, frowning.*

The dragon swung its head. The chain links rippled in the flashes of daylight streaking through the holes in the derelict roof.

Muuuuutthherrrrr.

The word rumbled around the stable. A tic developed at Brother Bernard's mouth. "*Mother?*" *he whispered.*

The dragon whimpered.

"*Then who is your father? Tell me,*" *said Bernard, his throat growing sore from the demands of a language so lacking in vowels.* "*Who is your father… Quickly. Your father?*"

The yellow eyes closed. The arches of the nostrils flared like trumpets. Gaaaawwwaaaaaainn, *said his distant descendant, Grockle.*

Bernard backed away with a hand against his throat.

Gawain.

That was all the proof he needed.

Meanwhile, 'Brother Vincent' is locked in his cell, and an off-island envoy sent for, to establish what should be done about the situation.

Unfortunately, when G'reth brought back the young Fain entity to this world, another Fain being came too. This one was a killer, out to punish G'reth's new-found friend, and to stop the fire star portal between Earth and the home thought-world of the Fain, Ki:mera, from opening. This entity took over the body of the envoy to Farlowe Island, desiring to find Grockle also, and cleanse this world of dragons. However, Grockle causes a fire, reclaims Gawain's claw, and escapes from the island, making his way to the Arctic, the Tooth of Ragnar, and the portal. The evil Fain follows. David is also in hot pursuit, using Bergstrom's invisible dragon, Groyne, to take him there through time and space.

Having reached the Tooth, David finds that Tootega is already there, but his body has been taken over by the killer Fain being. A dramatic confrontation occurs, with unforeseen results for David and all those connected to him.

Did Grockle make it through the portal in time? Why has Gwilanna been trapped as a raven in an ice block? What will Liz do when she discovers that Arthur's mind was entered by the evil Fain, leaving him terrified, confused and nearly blind? Did the young Fain escape its evil pursuer? And just what exactly is Bergstrom up to?

The Fire Eternal

Five years have passed since the end of *Fire Star*. David has been missing in the Arctic for all this time, and is presumed dead by all but Lucy. Despite this, daily life in the Crescent has returned to relative normality for the Pennykettles – and for Zanna, David's long-term partner, and their child, Alexa, who now both live with Lucy and Liz. Arthur has moved in too, having been nursed back to relative health by the family. He remains blind.

Alexa is nearly five. A very bright child, she has powers and awarenesses that are only just becoming apparent, and are yet to be taken seriously. On the anniversary of David's disappearance, Zanna presents Alexa with a gift.

"Listen carefully," said Zanna, dropping down on one knee. She brushed a curl of black hair off Alexa's forehead. "You know we talked about polar bears and the icy place they live?"

"Yes," said Alexa (possibly hopeful of receiving one).

Zanna looked at her a moment and tried to frame the words. Those eyes. His eyes. That rich dark blue. Unsettling and comforting, all in one glance. "Your daddy gave me a dragon there once. I want you to have him..." [Zanna] opened her hands – as if she was scattering the ashes of her grief – and set G'lant down on Alexa's palms.

The little girl looked thoughtfully at the space above her gloves. "I like him," she said.

This gesture seems to set Zanna free of some of her grief, and when a handsome young man called Tam Farrell appears to show an interest in her, she considers responding. Tam, however, is a journalist who has been contacted anonymously by Lucy, who believes it is high time that someone did something about trying to find David. She thinks Tam might be able to help in the search. Tam visits the shop that Zanna owns and buys a ('normal') clay dragon, while casually probing for information about David Rain.

It's not long before the Pennykettle dragons work out that Tam is not quite what he claims to be. Determined to put matters right, they set up a chain of events that result in Tam's girlfriend giving the game away to Zanna just before Tam is due to have a reflexology consultation with her. Zanna, of course, is angry and upset with Lucy, but with Tam especially.

"You know, for one foolish moment, I let myself believe that you could be something special, like David, when all you were giving me were lies and deceit."

"I can help you," [Tam] insisted… "If you tell the world the truth it will only raise your profile even more."

"Truth?" said Lucy. "What do you mean?"

Tam shook his head. "That he never existed. The author

of the book: David Rain, He's a cipher. It's all just a front, isn't it?"

In an attempt to prove Tam wrong, Lucy persuades him to take her to the address David wrote on his letter to Liz when responding to her original 'room for rent' advert.

However, events take a terrifying turn when, having got there, Lucy is pulled through a rift in space by an evil force. She finds herself on Farlowe Island, among the community of monks who live there. But the monks have been taken over, en masse, by the Ix.

The Ix are the negative version of the benevolent Fain, who use the power of fear to break down any resistance to their plans. They are particularly interested in Lucy because of her ancestry with dragons and her ability to create sculptures, inherited from her mother. They want her to make an anti-dragon from a compound called obsidian. The template for this creature, which they call a darkling, is generated from a hallucination based on Lucy's deepest dread.

In general shape it resembled a dragon. Serpentine body. Powerful wings. But it was thicker set and ugly. Cabbage ears. A gargoyle. Its feet and paws were stout, the claws inside them conical, tapering to points. It had no ordered rows of scales. Instead, the surface of its body was pocked and ridged as if the skin had been sheared from brittle rock. And apart from its pulsing, hooked green tongue and grey-tipped claws, it was completely black. Yet Lucy could see lightning spidering inside it, as though she had opened a box of mirrors. She shook her head in fear as the creature turned towards her. With a granite-like click it unlatched its jaw. From its throat came a bolt of pure black fire.

*

And when she has done that, they intend to send her back through the rift commingled with an Ix assassin...

In the meantime, David has found out a lot more about who and what he is, his history and his purpose on the planet. We also learn where he has been and what has happened to him in the past five years.

David is now in the Arctic, attempting to save his beloved polar bears – and indeed the world. He has teamed up with two of them, Kailar and Avrel, to search for the opening to the Fire Eternal, the most creative force in the Universe. David has in his possession the stone eye of Gawain, which has been brought up from the ocean depths by the sea goddess, Sedna. David intends to open the eye, and free the spirit of the dormant dragon at last.

David is also accompanied by Gwilanna, who was left as a raven and trapped in a block of ice at the end of the previous book. Despite being a nuisance, Gwilanna agrees to help David with his quest, on the promise of being returned to human form by the end of it.

However, events take a surprising turn when an ancient mammoth appears in front of them all.

David is quick to recognise it as a projection sent by his daughter, Alexa, as a token of her love. However, Kailar is hexed into perceiving it as something else.

Kailar gave out a fighting growl and immediately drew parallel to the mammoth's flank... He began pacing back and forth in a threatening manner, his head held low, his black tongue issuing from the side of his mouth. It was a gibe to the creature to come and challenge him.

Avrel tightened his claws. There was going to be trouble.

Indeed there was.

David urgently sends Gwilanna back to Wayward Crescent to protect Alexa when he realises that his daughter's auma trail must have been detected by the Ix, via the projection she sent. Gwilanna returns just in time to face the Ix:risor, or assassin, that is Lucy. There are devastating and far-reaching effects as a result of the confrontation, some of which echo throughout the rest of the series.

David, meanwhile, is nearing the end of his quest, and polar bears in their hundreds are gathering around the gateway to the Fire Eternal...

What does David intend to do with all the

congregated bears? Can he open Gawain's eye? Who does Lucy try to kill? And does she succeed? Which Pennykettle dragon is in dire danger of extinction? And why is an ornamental 'fairy door' so important? Will David ever return to Wayward Crescent?

Dark Fire

The last of the five books to be covered in this guide (remember there will be two more to finish the series) is the darkest of them all. It deals with (obviously!) dark fire, the most destructive force in the Universe.

The weather has gone completely weird; there is a mist over the Arctic that nothing can penetrate, and natural dragons are back to recolonise the Earth. As if all this worldwide hoo-ha wasn't enough to be getting on with, things are not so straightforward back in leafy suburbia either...

David appears unannounced one day in the Pennykettles' kitchen, where Zanna finds him sitting calmly at the table, apparently unconcerned about the upset his disappearance, and subsequent reappearance, has caused.

"Five years you were gone."
"I didn't know that."

"Five Christmases, five birthdays, five Father's Days, five...Valentine's." Five letters, she was thinking bitterly, remembering how she'd always written one to him on that day in mid-February, the anniversary of his apparent 'death'. *"And then you just turn up out of nowhere?"*

"I couldn't help it," he repeated. *"The Fain took me back. Into the world they call Ki:mera, a place where time is meaningless."*

"Not to me." She forced her pretty face forward. *"Just go, David. Disappear into your weird Fain world. Leave me alone to look after my child."*

Zanna is doubly upset as she has just discovered a strange rash on Alexa's back while bathing her. The little girl doesn't seem to be troubled by it, but it is yet one more thing to add to the growing list of anxieties that pervade the Pennykettle household.

Liz is pregnant again, this time naturally, and Lucy is not her old self at all. Although the Ix assassin within her has gone, she is still feeling guilty and in shock about what it made her do. As if all this wasn't enough, Henry, the Pennykettles' cranky next-door neighbour, is ill and his sister, Agatha, arrives to look after him. Agatha turns out to be another sibyl, one of many that seem to be popping up all over the world as the twelve natural dragons from the old Wearle, or colony, are being awakened from their prolonged 'sleep'.

The whereabouts of these dragons' resting places is

becoming the subject of intense interest since Arthur received a phone call from an old friend, Rupert Steiner. Rupert has been visited by a small dragon, later identified as Gadzooks, who has left a message on a piece of Steiner's best notepaper.

Arthur, with Liz and Lucy (and Lucy's special dragon, Gwendolen – along for the ride as satnav) go to see Rupert at his home in Cambridge. There, with Gwendolen's help, they discover that Gadzooks had written the word 'Scuffenbury' – but in dragontongue. Steiner recalls that he has seen some similar marks in some photographs he was once sent, taken in a cave at a place called the Hella glacier, in the Arctic. Using Gadzooks' message as a key, he ultimately manages to decipher the writings on the wall of the cave. They turn out to be the record of a meeting between the last twelve dragons in the world (*The Last Dragon Chronicles*, in fact). The writings are subsequently published by Tam in his newspaper's magazine.

Lucy is thoroughly thrown by what she learns from this article. It becomes obvious that one of these twelve dragons is lying dormant at Scuffenbury, beneath a hill called Glissington Tor. David persuades Lucy to go there with Tam.

"I've booked us in here."

"The Old Grey Dragon?"

"It's a guest house," [Tam] said. *"Bed and Breakfast.*

Right on the side of the Tor. It says in their blurb that on a still night you can hear the dragon snoring. I thought it might make you feel at home."

But 'at home' is the last thing that Lucy feels. A terrifying nightmare whilst asleep on the first night is followed by a series of further nightmares in broad daylight. The owners of the guest house, Hannah and Clive, *seem* perfectly pleasant people; the only other guest, a Ms Gee, while a little eccentric and 'offish' *appears* to want nothing more than to be left alone; and as for *the cat* – well, the guest house owners deny any knowledge of a cat…

It all starts off innocently enough with Tam and Lucy deciding to take a walk up the hill opposite the Tor, to spy out the land. Lucy, looking across the valley, spots something out of the ordinary.

"I think there's someone on the Tor."

His footsteps halted. She saw him squint in that scary polar bear fashion, just the way David sometimes did. "Probably a tourist. People come here all the time." He started along the path again, almost bounding where it hollowed out into a dip.

Lucy scrabbled after him, glancing at the figure every now and then. Comparatively speaking it was nothing but a matchstick, but Lucy, blessed with the eyesight of youth, could still work out its basic movements. She saw the arms come parallel with the shoulders. Half-stretched, not full, as if the person might be cupping their hands above their eyes. Or holding a pair of binoculars.

But things deteriorate rapidly from there, especially once they discover that the person watching them is yet another sibyl.

And speaking of sibyls, Gwilanna has gone missing, along with the isoscele of Gawain and an obsidian knife, which she had stolen from the Ix that had invaded Lucy. David is keen to find Gwilanna, not only because she is highly dangerous in her own right, but also because the knife contains a spark of dark fire. The leader of the new Wearle, a natural dragon called G'Oreal, insists the dark fire be taken north to be destroyed.

David solicits Zanna's help in locating Gwilanna, and Zanna obliges by tracking and following the sibyl to Farlowe Island. Once there, Zanna finds she has walked into a trap. Gwilanna is in a maudlin mood, lamenting the fact that she should have been granted illumination (a spiritual merging) with the offspring of a dragon called Ghislaine, but was cheated out of it. Gwilanna has created a force-field around the circle of standing stones in the middle of the island, within which Zanna, and the dark fire, are held.

"The circle will magnify the spark behind you and the Fain will see it from here to Ki:mera. By the time they

133

*arrive, I will be gone – with the obsidian – and my terms will
be written in your blood across the stones: give me
illumination – or I take the dark fire to the Ix."*

But Gwilanna's plans go awry, and the spell that was
intended to put the spectre of the dragon Ghislaine to
rest instead attracts the auma of a very different – and
terrifying – creature. A flock of ravens roosting nearby
are also affected by the energy flow and begin to
mutate…with far-reaching consequences.

These raven-mutants cause mayhem and destruction
wherever they go. But in the initial confusion at the
stone circle, the one saving grace is that Gwilanna,
although still free, has been forced to leave the dark
fire behind. This Zanna gives to David, who retains it
for his own purposes, rather than take it north to the
Wearle, as directed. But possession of the dark fire
brings interest from the Ix. Zanna is concerned that the
Ix are too much of a threat in a general sense, and is
worried for the family's safety specifically. David
decides to tell her more about the situation.

*"You're right, the Ix can't be defeated, as such – but their
negative auma can be transmuted… When they're
concentrated into a conglomerate they become almost
impossible for the human mind to resist. But that's exactly
the state we need them in: one huge cluster. It's getting them
there that's the difficult part."*

"And whose finger will be on the trigger when you do? I've never seen that mangy crone Gwilanna scared until she talked about you meddling with the Fire Eternal."

"It won't be me," he said, and looked at her hard.

Slowly, the implication in his gaze began to register. "No," she said, covering the scars on her arm. "If you put Alexa in any kind of danger, I'll—"

"Alexa is already in danger," he said, with a calmness she found unsettling. To her deeper dismay, she realised she was trying hard not to cry.

The danger for the whole family continues to increase. Even Sophie (David's first girlfriend) emails from Africa to say that she thinks something is amiss with her 'special' dragon, Grace. The tension builds; breaking-point is imminent.

Back at Scuffenbury, Lucy succeeds in awakening the dormant dragon there, but with drastic effect and at great cost to herself and those around her. Tam is missing, several others are dead, and although David sends Grockle to help her, she finds that that help may be too little and too late.

When she looked again, Glissington Tor had broken into four distinct mounds, and rising from its smoking centre was the most terrifying dragon she had ever seen.

It was green, savage, and at least three times the size of Grockle. When it threw out its wings it blinded the sun and seemed to draw the landscape around it like a blanket. From

nostril to tail it must have measured half a small field. For a moment or two it kept its head folded into its chest, but when it raised its snout and Lucy saw the redness in one eye, the bones at the base of her spine turned to jelly. The dragon had been horribly attacked at some time. Or maybe something had failed with its fire tear? Or the eye had become diseased in some way? She couldn't tell. Nor could she bear to look at it for long. But little did she know she would soon be forced to…
The scales around its neck came up in a frill and black smoke gushed from its long, narrow snout. Paying no heed whatsoever to Grockle, it turned its damaged gaze on Lucy. At first she told herself it couldn't have seen her. She had to be a mile and a half away at least. But with a wallop of wings that tickled the blades of grass around her feet, the thing took off and headed their way. In mid-flight, it uncoupled its jaw and let out a squeal that sounded like a pig being forced through a grinder. Lucy saw Grockle tense. The squeal gathered force and grew into a roar, which seemed loud enough to shatter the dome of the sky. Lucy covered her ears and screamed.

The arrival on the scene of darklings and hordes of Ix entities intensifies the situation even further and a full-scale battle commences in the skies over Scuffenbury.

Dun-dun-dunnnn… You know what to do to find out whether Lucy – or any of the other characters – survive or not. What happens to Liz's child – if indeed it is a child? What fate has Gwilanna brought upon herself?

Lucy meets her destiny

What is the 'new species' that is to be introduced into the world, according to David? Will Mother Earth herself turn against its human occupants if the Ix win the battle and an inversion occurs? Will the light of the world turn finally to an eternal dark?...

This chapter has been a very swift run-through of some of the funny and some of the exciting storylines. There are many more that I have deliberately barely mentioned, or not even touched on, as that will leave a lot more for you to discover and to enjoy for yourselves.

In books one to five we meet, respectively, squirrels, polar bears, monks, alien thought-beings, and darklings (not to mention a unicorn). If you like any or all of these, you'll probably like these stories. And it might go without saying that these books are certainly for you if you can't get enough of:

DRAGONS!

Chapter 9: Whistlers, Wastrels and Woebegones*

If you ask Chris what he believes *The Last Dragon Chronicles* is really about, he will not answer you with 'squirrels', 'polar bears', or even 'dragons'; he will say 'creativity'.

Like almost every other person alive, Chris questions who he is and where he 'fits' in this world. Unlike most people, however, he explores this via the medium of writing, 'trying characters and ideas on' to see if they have any resonance. Are they *him*?

Sometimes, we have conflicting parts of us that want different things – one part wanting ice cream and another part wanting jelly, for instance. As an author, Chris can not only have both, but also feel no personal conflict about it, as his characters do the 'wanting' for him. His characters are, in truth, facets of his own self, held up to the light for examination. Thus, in these books, Chris is actually exploring his own psyche.

Anything is possible

Chris has found, like any other author, that in a story he can be whoever he wants, do whatever he wants, and go wherever he wants, with no boundaries and no

* *This is what Gwilanna disparagingly calls storytellers.*

limits. Another human being? An animal? A tree? A nail in a floorboard? No problem: anything is possible. It is relatively easy for him to describe polar bears, for example, as he knows what they look like. But the trick to being a great writer is to go beyond that and 'become' that bear. To describe its thoughts, feelings and actions from the inside, as it lives them itself.

This is what Chris likes to do; in fact, he claims that if he were to be an animal, a polar bear is exactly what he would choose to be. His love and respect for them is clear in the stories.

The creation of the character David Rain, which is based on Chris as a young man, allows Chris to take a look at himself from a distance, and decide whether he likes what he sees. If not, it can all be changed.

David Rain…sometimes

Creating characters, in general, is a way to look at yourself, your life, your beliefs, your feelings, 'safely' and without fear of being laughed at or ridiculed. After all, it's not *you*, is it? For young people, it's possible to test things out via someone you've created, before committing yourself to those things in real life. Not sure whether you'd fancy being a doctor? Write about one, and see. Feeling awkward about talking to your mum about something? Try it out on paper first.

When he was a boy, Chris always fancied being a pop star, a footballer or an astronaut. Needless to say, none of those things happened – he didn't want them enough. These days, he still likes to write songs but only watches football on TV (it needs less energy, he says). Having a ride in the space shuttle remains a dream, but now, as a writer, he could easily experience any of those childhood fancies at the touch of a key.

David Rain starts out as a naïve, innocent young man, with a clean slate as far as his ideas about himself and his world are concerned. He has none, really. But over the course of a little more than five years, book-time, he goes on a staggering personal journey to become something beyond his wildest imaginings. Something he didn't even know it was possible to be (read the books to find out exactly what). Through writing *The Last Dragon Chronicles*, Chris's life, too, has changed and expanded, often beyond his own expectations. He's very grateful to his alter ego, David Rain.

Inspiration

Since becoming a writer (of songs and stories) the one question Chris has wrangled with is this: where does inspiration come from? The creation of Gadzooks as a character was meant to answer that. Gadzooks is the tangible physical manifestation of 'the fire within', the creative force that resides within us all. Gadzooks represents that part of us that does have all the answers – if only we could access them. Zookie, as he is affectionately called, enables David to do just that. As long as he trusts his faithful dragon and the words he writes on his pad, all is well – eventually!

The crucial thing in the stories that is emphasised repeatedly is that David *loves* Gadzooks, that he must never make him cry, so that he won't shed his fire tear, or lose his spark. In other words, David must keep Zookie's inner flame alight. In day to day terms, Chris is telling himself to 'stay friends' with his creative source, or he will run the risk of losing its help, and with it the ability to be inspired. Believing in Gadzooks 'raises his auma', that is, makes the connection to David stronger. The more that happens, the easier the connection is maintained. Self-belief is vital for a writer.

Gadzooks is also a vehicle to open David's mind to possibilities beyond those that would usually be considered the accepted norm. Likewise, by following his own intuition, Chris can create his own pathway through the world, literary or otherwise, instead of simply re-tracing the old familiar tracks of habit.

As if all that wasn't enough, Zookie is able to predict the future – only a very short while ahead – *or* he makes the future happen, or perhaps a little of both. In the book, it is deliberately ambivalent as to whether fiction is mirroring life, or vice versa. Chris is telling himself that circumstances are not always definitely one thing or another. Sometimes they are much more complex than that; wisdom often lies in keeping an open mind.

The creative process

Chris often finds vital bits of information for a story just 'popping up' at the exact moment he needs them. This happens far too many times to ignore. He now just accepts it as part of the creative process. And if the information isn't to hand, a quick request to the Universe (that is, a mental plea sent out for help) usually brings what is required, and often from very unlikely sources.

Chris 'trusts Gadzooks' in the sense that he often doesn't know what he's writing about until after he's done it. To paraphrase David, when he describes writing his stories to Liz, "It's a bit like being on a mystery tour… You sort of know that you're going, but you can't be sure where until you arrive."

Chris will write anywhere. (Not on walls in subways, of course.) When away from home, he has to make do with any odd moment that he can find, at any time of day, or even night, sometimes, to type on his laptop. Ideally, however, Chris writes in the mornings, till around two-thirty if 'in the zone'. An average of 500–1,000 words is considered to be a 'good' day – but on a 'bad' day, he'll stare at the carpet till ten, cut his fingernails for fifteen minutes, decide it's imperative that he rearrange his paperclips (individually) for a further hour. Then he'll have a change of pace and strum his guitar, waiting for inspiration to come. Clearly, though, it's inspiration's day off: it will take Chris forty-three minutes and twenty-two seconds to realise this. (He'll be watching the hands of the clock by now.) Eventually, he will write a paragraph. Rewrite it. Erase some of it. Replace it in a different order. Erase all of it. Snarl a bit. Growl a bit. Write it again. Then he'll come downstairs having achieved nothing but an oversized headache. Thankfully, days like these are few and far between.

However, on those days when he does get 'into the zone' – lost in that other world – he can hardly get the words out quickly enough. The story flows and pours out of him almost faster than he can write it down. Chris says this is the biggest 'high' in the world. Time ceases to exist for him, and even when he comes downstairs for something to eat he is still in a daze and has to take time out to readjust to this world. It is almost as if the story has already been written on some other plane of existence, and Chris is just 'listening' and copying it down. As if the story itself is a living entity and wants to be told, just as much as Chris wants to tell it. It's a co-operative venture, he says.

Other authors have spoken of a similar feeling, that they have to just 'reach up' and grab a story 'out of the ether'. This could explain why many books on a particular subject (say, vampires, wizards, dragons) are created at similar times. Some will be just 'jumping on the bandwagon' of something that has been proven to be a recent commercial success, but discounting that, there is a definite 'zeitgeist' (meaning 'spirit of the time') effect going on. A basic idea seems to make itself known to any who are able to perceive it 'floating around', but each person filters it through their own personality and writing style, so different authors will have different 'takes' on it, and thus will turn out different books, but all with the same theme.

Chris is interested in many different subjects 'beyond the boundaries' of accepted reality, and explores them in his writing. Subjects such as quantum mechanics, time (is there such a thing?) travel, probable realities, parallel universes (are there other versions of 'us'?), life (with or without physical bodies) on other worlds and the expansion of consciousness all appeal to him hugely. He has always had an attraction to such topics and investigates them in his imagination before including them in his fiction. But is it fiction? Could it be that we *do* choose our own parents, as Alexa does, or that death *is* 'just another place to be'? Can we heal ourselves simply by the power of thought? Or affect the outcome of situations just by intention?

Our understanding of this world is changing all the time, and there are a larger and larger number of scientists who are now beginning to think that some, if not all, of these things may be within our capabilities as human beings, at some point in the future, if not currently (some say there is only an eternal 'now'). Perhaps in days or years or centuries to come, extra sensory perception – things like telepathy, manifesting by visualisation, conversing with flowers and the apparently inanimate Universe – will be commonplace. Perhaps there really is a fine line between what you imagine and what you create. In which case, we had all better start imagining wonderful things – and thus do our part towards creating a wonderful world in which to live in peace and harmony. As David Rain says, "All things are possible with The Fire Eternal", the most creative force in the Universe.

Chapter 10: Online

Most authors have a website these days; Chris is no exception. The official Chris d'Lacey website, www.icefire.co.uk, and was created by Marshall Pinsent at www.pinsentdesign.com, virtually (ha!) from scratch. Chris gave him all the info, of course, but the rest was entirely Marsh's brainchild.

On this site, you can find out masses about Chris and his books, as well as a link to dragon-maker extraordinaire Valerie Chivers. Her contact details are val@valchivers.co.uk in case you want to purchase one of her little masterpieces. Chris's website is also 'home' to Gadzooks' own literary output, a blog called Zookie's Notepad. Zookie updates this each Sunday, and it usually contains tales of delight or of woe regarding the doings and failings of Chris himself, whom Zookie calls 'the author'. He occasionally puts paw to pencil to mention 'Mrs author' too, usually representing me in a rather better light than Chris, for some reason.

He thinks Chris is a bit too slow on the uptake sometimes, often ignores what he has written on his pad and even misses the fact that it is his genius that makes the books what they are. He's also a bit miffed that Snigger the squirrel got a handsome royalty of ten per cent (paid in nuts) when *The Fire Within* came out, yet he, Zookie, has seen nary a bean for all his efforts.

Maybe that's why he was so delighted when I told him he was to have his picture published.

Gadzooks in superstar mode; pad and pencil aside, for once

Along with hints and tips for budding writers, the icefire website also houses Chris's contact details (for fan mail and for event bookings), a list of frequently asked questions – and some of Chris's songs which relate to the books, more about which in Chapter 11.

Also worth a visit is the website set up specially for Chris by his publishers: the address is www.thelastdragonchronicles.com and this includes a character list similar to the one in this guidebook, as well as more general info on Chris and his dragon books.

Chris receives between one hundred and two hundred emails a week from fans all over the world. He does his very best to answer each one individually, though this is occasionally difficult to do when he is away travelling or deep in the home stretch of book-writing. Very rarely he'll send a generic response letter, but he dislikes doing so quite intensely. He believes that if a fan has taken the trouble to write to him, then he should do them the honour of replying personally. Ages of fans range from eight to eighty-eight (to our definite knowledge) and the messages cover a whole spectrum from a simple 'I think your dragon books are the best!' to great missives that are almost books in their own right. All are welcome. As Chris says, it is only by this kind of feedback that you know you're doing a good job – or not.

Although the majority of emails are from young people, a growing number are from adults, often thanking Chris for his books from a parent's point of view. These are the ones where a child with severe dyslexia, for instance, has improved because they couldn't wait for their mum or dad to read them the next instalment of the story, so have picked it up themselves and persisted through their difficulties, as they just *had* to know what happened next. It is life-changing for Chris, as well as the child concerned, when he reads messages like these. The satisfaction is enormous, both on a creative level, and simply as a human being.

Some of the emails are incredibly funny, whether intentionally or not. Like the young lad who wrote to Chris thanking him for coming to talk at his school, saying how much he'd enjoyed the visit, and how Chris had 'expired' him. We assume he meant 'inspired', as we have had no visits from the local police force regarding 'death by reading *Icefire*'.

Another lamented the fact that he could not see and converse with dragons; his school did not have a language class in dragontongue…

A third, from a ten-year-old, wanted to know Chris's best chat-up line. Rather taken aback, Chris responded that he was born on an island in the Mediterranean Sea called Malta, which made him a kind of Malteser. He would therefore go up to a girl and ask her if she 'fancied a Malteser'. It's fortunate that the boy didn't ask whether it worked or not. We still wonder whether he tried it out for himself. A bit too birthplace-specific, perhaps.

Chris once put a picture of his breakfast bowl up on his site; no particular reason – the camera was just handy when he was having his soggies, so he thought, *Why not?* You would not believe the amount of email traffic that caused. Everyone and his wife wanted to know what was in the bowl. Even teachers were writing in, saying they had been taking bets on it being this cereal or that one. Just what is all that about? And no, I'm not telling you what brand it was. We might just be inundated.

Chris recalled reading about a famous pop star in the 1960s being quoted in an interview as liking jelly babies. The star had sackloads sent to him by adoring fans over the next five years. Every time the interview appeared in a different paper or magazine, another batch would arrive. Although Chris doesn't go so far as to imagine he has even one *adoring* fan, he quite fancies the idea of mentioning that he likes liquorice, and fruit and nut chocolate – just in case.

And while we're on the subject of the 1960s, one bright spark asked Chris if he liked the Beatles. Thinking that he had acquired some strange sort of telepathic link with said child, he replied, 'Why yes, how clever of you to realise. Indeed I do.' Immediately came back the response, 'Thought so. All *old* people like the Beatles...' Oops. That didn't go down too well in d'Lacey-world.

We had one message from a lad (who shall remain nameless) who told Chris endless information about himself; where he lived, who he lived with, what their names, habits and hobbies were; what his ambitions were; on and on. It was actually quite interesting. But right at the end of page four or thereabouts, he finished up with a final sentence, apropos of nothing, thus:

'What was your favourite swimming stroke at school?'

It had absolutely nothing to do with the bulk of the email, and left us both mystified, speechless, and then hysterical with laughter, in that order.

Chris does have some quite 'normal' ones, in case you think he just attracts the rather strange kind. 'Were you good at writing when you were at school?' is a common one. The answer is yes – and no. Take a look at Chris's school report, pictured. The real one actually read, 'Chris's grammar is outstanding, but sadly this boy *does not have a creative thought in his head.*' Chris was dropped down a flight of stairs when he was a baby; it obviously took thirty years for the concussion to wear off. Either that, or his creative ideas were in his socks all the time. You will also note that he was rubbish at Geography, too. That is precisely why he made David a Geography student. Just as well he did, because it was a very useful and believable way to get our hero to the Arctic – on a field trip for college.

Geography	Has yet to learn that one cannot eat one's dinner off a tectonic plate.	J.L.
English	... this boy does not have a creative thought in his head.	E.H
Chemistry	Progress at last. d'Lacey has only tried to blow up the lab once this term.	J.H

See me afterwards, boy!

152

'Who is your favourite character to write?' is another regular enquiry. The response tends to be either Gwilanna, the sibyl, or Gretel, the potions dragon. Chris says it's always more fun to write the baddies or the rebels. More to get your literary teeth into, apparently.

And talking of things literary, 'What are your top ten favourite sentences that you have written in the books?' had Chris scratching his head, if not his teeth. He came up with *'Who are you?'*... *'Your destiny.'* (as asked by David and responded to by Anders Bergstrom) in *Icefire*, Gretel trying to blow smoke rings through Bonnington's ears, and the tundra being described as the *'unshaved face of God'*, (both from *Fire Star*) as the first three.

The other seven favourites all came from *Dark Fire*. Whether this is because it has much more memorable lines in it, or simply that Chris had not long finished that book and thus it was still fresh in his mind, is open to question.

And the seven? Gwendolen as satnav; *'the god that is Pod'*; extreme ironing; *'the gorilla's burned the sausages'*; *'not in the curriculum of motherhood'*; the Earth being ready for a new species, and (a bit of a cheat because it was way longer than a sentence), the description of David with his frockcoat and gunslinger look. This last one would always be in any of Chris's top tens as he would love to wear a similar outfit himself (though with strictly no gunslinging, of course). Failing that, he would have wanted to be Fox Mulder from *The X-Files* – it's Fox's interest in the unknown and the unusual that is the attraction there.

The 'short-and-sweet' queries are great fun. Often an email will come in with no mention of the books, and with only a dozen or so words in the message: 'Describe yourself in three words' (*tall, daft and handsome*); 'Why should I get my mum to buy me a Pennykettle dragon?' (*They warm the place up, do toast in a flash – albeit a bit blackened – and reheat a cup of tea quicker than any microwave.*) 'Who would you give your last Rolo to?' (*Gadzooks*); 'What was your first job?' (*Screwing the handles onto coffins* – Chris's grandad was an undertaker – *then later working in a toilet roll factory – as a tester…*of the perforations, of course. What did you think he meant?); 'If David is based on you, do you say *tee-hee-hee* and *crikey*, like David does?' (*Yes, I do* – I can vouch for this; he also snores just like David is described as doing); 'What is your perfect sandwich?' (*Lancashire cheese with lashings of brown sauce – but as a child: peaches, crisps, sugar and liquorice torpedos* – it is unclear whether Chris meant separately, or as one almighty melange. And I honestly haven't had the courage to ask him. *Far* too much information.)

But there are two questions that stand out from all the thousands of those that Chris has been asked. The first of these is:

'Where do you want your ashes scattered when you die?'

As it happened, Chris had a ready (and truthful) answer – the library gardens in Bromley – but for sheer originality that conversation-stopper certainly gets its enquirer ten out of ten.

The query in the second one was straightforward enough:

'If you went to a desert island, who or what would you leave behind?'

But it stands out more for Chris's reply:

'A misleading note giving my incorrect whereabouts.'

Perhaps it was just one question too many that day.

Chapter 11: All Fired Up

One of the great advantages of being an author is to be able to meet the fans as well as just hear from them by letter or email. Chris used to love signing autographs and in the dim and distant past would practise his signature endlessly (or so it seemed) in hopes of 'just once' being asked to sign a book or two. Time and circumstances have changed, and now he gets writer's cramp just thinking about it. The record for the most number of books signed in a single session currently stands at around seven hundred, I believe.

In these numbers, Chris will only sign his name, but if he has the time he will also add a dedication – the person's name and a short message, too. Incidentally, we only found out the other day that a book signed by the author but with no other wordage added is more valuable than one signed *to* someone.

The only exception here, apparently, is if there is what is called 'good provenance' in a dedication. This means that if the book was signed to someone who was famous in their own right, say, and it could be proved that the dedication was genuine, then that would be worth more than a book with the author's signature alone. Of course, a personal message is always worth more to the individual that any monetary value that could be put upon it, and quite rightly so. Chris has twice signed books with messages in a foreign language: German and Welsh. He had to learn them deliberately before he started, but the recipients were surprised and delighted.

And while we're on the subject, *The Last Dragon Chronicles* are themselves available in a number of different languages. The countries where translated editions are published include Germany, Romania, the Czech Republic, Hungary, Japan and the United States. Yes, you read that correctly, the dragon books are *translated* into American. In practise, this means that as well as 'sidewalk' substituted for 'pavement' and similar changes, the settings are altered too (the stories in the US editions are based in Massachusetts and New York, rather than in Kent and London, for instance).

In fact, in *Dark Fire*, it was actually necessary to invent an entirely new landscape for Scuffenbury Hill. There are no chalk hills anywhere in the United States, so one was created specially, in New England!

As some of the plotlines are also adjusted slightly to make sense to the American reader, it is quite an interesting process to check out one version against the other. The changes in plotline are made by Chris himself, but the 'language' and setting changes are done by his American publishers.

The dragon books are incredibly popular in the United States. Chris now wishes he had tacked a map of that country up on the wall, so he could stick a pin in for every state that he'd had an email from. He thinks it must be every single one by now. It would certainly seem so, as the series has consistently appeared on the *New York Times* bestsellers lists.

The foreign editions are beautiful creations. Some have a few black and white line drawings in them, but the Japanese versions are awesome. As well as line drawings, they also have full colour illustrations at the front of the book. Or rather, the 'back' of the book, as we would perceive it, as the Japanese language is written in ideographs (glyphs or 'pictures') and read from top to bottom and right to left, in columns. So starting in the top-right corner, you would read down the rightmost column first, then go back up to the top of the page and read the column next left till you get to the bottom of the page again, and so on. Thus you would appear to be reading the book backwards when compared to the way we are used to, here in the UK.

All the translations for foreign editions are done in the country of publication (Chris is ace at English and passable in dragontongue and felinespeak, but useless at any other languages), and according to friends who have read the books in their own native language and in English, they are pretty faithful to the originals. Translations do not seem to pose too much of a barrier for those doing them, except that once Chris had a frantic email from the Japanese translator, desperate to know what 'daft as a brush' meant. The complicated plotlines and esoteric mysticisms were easy-peasy, allegedly, but that one had them stumped. Colloquial English is a tricky idiom to explain, even for the English native speaker, and Chris did his best, but he'd love to know how that phrase was expressed, in the end.

The Fire Within – Czech Republic

Icefire – Germany

Fire Star – Japan

The Fire Eternal – UK

The Dragons of Wayward Crescent

Chris is writing an offshoot of the original novels, for younger readers mainly, though it seems all age groups (including adults) are enjoying them, from the feedback received. Each book features one of the Pennykettle dragons and tells the story of its creation and its own special ability. All of these 'little' books are stand-alone, but numbered on the spines, so they can be read in the 'correct' order if so desired. There are also letters on the UK edition spines which, when the books are placed upright on a shelf in order of publication, will spell something out.

Again, I won't spoil the surprise by letting you in on the secret now. The four books currently published are about *Gruffen*, *Gauge*, *Glade* and *Grabber*, the first three of whom appear in *The Last Dragon Chronicles* series. The *Wayward Crescent* series, taken together, is meant as a prequel to *The Fire Within*, as they are all set in the Pennykettle household before David arrives as their lodger. They also fill in a lot of background history to the Pennykettles and their dragons, which is what has piqued the interest of some people from older age groups.

The songs

Chris has also recorded a couple of songs relating to the

original *Last Dragon Chronicles* series. Called *Fire Star* and *The Fire Eternal*, they can be found on Chris's website (www.icefire.co.uk), but as yet they are not available to download (though this may change if any record companies take an interest!). All instruments are played by Chris, and all the vocals are his too, but sung from David's point of view. The lyrics are as follows, for those of you who are interested:

Fire Star

There is a sign in the heavens
Another light in the darkness
A better time is beginning
There is a fire star coming

I see the mark of the ice bear
In the tears of the dragon
And you'd better start wishing
There is a fire star coming

Stay with me, my love…

There is a sign in the heavens
Another light in the darkness
And you'd better start wishing
There is a fire star coming

The Fire Eternal

It's like breathing in several degrees of the sun
The ice and the fire all rolled into one
And look at the shape of the man you've become
It ain't easy, touching the sky
It ain't easy, learning to die
It ain't easy, stepping outside of the circle
Into the fire eternal

How could you think this is all we were worth?
My love for you beats at the heart of the Earth
I was around with the stars at their birth
It ain't easy, turning the page
It ain't easy, taking the stage
It ain't easy, facing the final rehearsal
Before the fire eternal

And hey, what you thought was finality
Preys on your fears of mortality
Here, in this changing reality world
Stand on the edge of the light with me
Take in the wonders of flight with me
in this calling, truth and love are one… om

Atoms and dust at the core of your star
But what you perceive here is not what you are
The journey to wisdom is not very far
It ain't easy, taking the stage

It ain't easy, turning the page
It ain't easy, stepping outside of the circle
Into the fire eternal
Into the fire eternal
Love is the fire eternal...

The first line of the Fire Eternal lyric was inspired by a line David speaks in *Dark Fire*, in response to a question that Zanna asks.

Chris also has several other songs, unrelated to the Last Dragon Chronicles, posted on the internet at www.myspace.com/chrisdlacey.

And for those few of you who have been astute enough to notice the dots at the beginning and end of the poem at the conclusion of the third book, *Fire Star*, yes, that does mean that the published lines are only a snippet of a longer piece. They are an abridged (and slightly adapted) version of a poem Chris wrote, again from David's point of view, called 'G'lant'. G'lant is an invisible dragon, given to Zanna by David when he has been pierced through the heart with a spear of ice. For the first time in print, here it is in full:

G'lant
That night I gave you a Valentine dragon,
a fissure opened deep within the Earth
and all below me tilted. Frosted crystals

chimed the air, melting on your tender kiss
as all your warmth and bliss came mine,
for one degree of sway, of time.

On that beat, my heart struck up
a plangent chord and drew
whatever magma rose to light
that single shining spark within
your dark, breathtaking eyes.
So brown, so like the Earth herself.
This moving ground, this slanted shelf.

Here is my quest: my pledge to you:
that life and all its tangled plights
could not call down a single wake
to quench this dragon's winter task.
Until the stars have blinked their last,
wherever on this Earth you walk,
he will arouse, excite, inspire,
and keep alight that spark,
this fire.

What comes next?

As previously mentioned, there will be two further
books following *Dark Fire* to conclude *The Last Dragon
Chronicles*. As I type, Chris has got over seventy-six

thousand words of the sixth book written already. It is called *Fire World*, and by the time you read this, he will have finished it completely. He has a rough idea of how the series will end, and a tentative title for the seventh book, but is still being surprised himself by what is turning up, so this may have changed entirely by publication day.

I've managed to persuade him to let me snaffle a sneak preview for you, to give a taste of what is coming. Once again, *Fire World* will have a totally different 'feel' from each of the other five, and it begins when 'David' is twelve years old, and having strange dreams. He has been seen by Counsellor Strømberg, who has recommended that he spend some time away from the world in seclusion at a place called Bushley Librarium. Harlan and Eliza are David's parents.

It rose out of the flowers like a great grey monolith. A single tall building with an uncountable number of floors. The upper floors were lost in wisps of cloud and the whole structure seemed to be bending backwards as though it had reached a critical mass and was ready to topple over at any moment. Fine red sand (or something like it) was raining down from the joints in the brickwork and being taken away in skirts on the breeze. At ground level there was just one door. It was made of wood (unusually) and was twice Harlan's height. It was already halfway open, despite the fact that a small sign badly attached to the right of the door frame invited visitors to R NG THE BE L. Harlan moved forward to do just that and stepped on something that had spilled out of the doorway. It was a large-format book. He reached down and picked it up. It must have been twenty years since he'd seen one. He smoothed a film of the red sand off the glossy cover and handed it to Eliza.

"The Art of Baking Cakes," she read.

Harlan shrugged. "Welcome to the librarium."

Eliza opened the pages and looked at several of the ancient digigrafs. "Why do we keep this stuff? I could easily imagineer anything in this. I don't understand what use this is to anyone."

"Historical value," Harlan said. He took the book from her and flipped through its pages. He showed a digigraf of a chocolate gateau to David. The boy's eyes lit up and he quickly imagineered a miniature version. He gave it to his mother.

Eliza smiled and deconstructed it. "Bad for your purity of vision," she said.

"I think books are rather quaint," said Harlan. "And they're real, of course, not constructs." He closed the book and – for want of anywhere better to put it – simply laid it in the grass. "Our ancestors would have relied on these things."

Eliza shook her head and looked up at the building again. "Is all of it real, do you think?"

Harlan nodded. He touched the brickwork, feeling its

roughness, though that in itself was no proof of authenticity; anyone could imagineer a brick. "Mmm. Probably. I doubt whether the curator would have enough in his fain to put up something so large – and be able to maintain it."

Eliza sighed and put her hand on David's shoulders, pulling him back towards her a little. "Why would Strømberg send him to a relic like this?"

"Well, let's begin the process of finding out." And this time, Harlan did press the bell.

The last word

I trust you've found this potter through *The Last Dragon Chronicles* and its author's life entertaining and informative, but I really can't finish this book without a last word from Gadzooks – which is, of course, "*hrrr*"...

Turn the page for a taste of the first book in

The
Last Dragon
Chronicles

The
Fire
Within

Chris d'Lacey

Welcome to Wayward Crescent

"Well, here we are," Mrs Pennykettle said, pausing by the door of the room she had for rent. She clasped her hands together and smiled. "Officially, it's our dining room, but we always eat in the kitchen these days."

The young man beside her nodded politely and patiently adjusted his shoulder bag. "Lovely. Erm, shall we take a look…?"

"It used to be our junk room, really," said a voice.

Mrs Pennykettle clucked like a hen.

The visitor turned. A young girl was lolling in the kitchen doorway. She was dressed in jeans and a sloppy top and had wet grass sticking to the heels of her trainers. "All our rammel's in the attic now."

"And where have *you* been?" Mrs Pennykettle said.

"In the garden," said the girl, "looking for Conker."

"Conkers?" the young man queried. "Aren't you a week or two early for them?"

"Not *ers*," said the girl, "*er*."

The visitor furrowed his brow.

Mrs Pennykettle sighed and did the introductions: "David, this is Lucy, my daughter. I'm afraid she comes as part of the package. Lucy, this is David. He's here to see the room."

Lucy chewed a wisp of her straw-coloured hair and slowly looked the visitor up and down.

Her mother tried again: "We've done the room out as best we can. There's a table in the corner, with a study lamp, of course, and a wardrobe we bought from a second-hand shop. The bed's not brilliant, but you should be all right if you try to avoid the loose spring in the middle."

"Mum?"

"*What?*"

"Why don't you stop twittering and *show* him?" With a huff, Lucy stomped down the hall to join them. "She's not always like this," she said to David. "It's because we've never had a lodger before." Before her mother could "twitter" in protest, Lucy reached out and pushed the door open. David smiled graciously and stepped inside. The fresh smell of lavender wafted through the room, mingled with the peaceful tinkle of wind chimes. Everything was perfect, exactly as described. Except…

"What's that?" David pointed to a bulge in the bed.

Elizabeth Pennykettle groaned with embarrassment. She swept across the room and dived beneath the folds of the red patterned duvet.

"That's Bonnington, our cat," Lucy said, grinning. "He likes getting under things – newspapers, duvets, all sorts of stuff. Mum says he's always getting under her feet."

David smiled and put down his bag. "Bonnington. That's a really good name for a cat."

Lucy nodded in agreement. "Mum named him after a mountain climber. I don't know why; he couldn't climb a beanbag. Well, he *could*, but we don't have one. He mistakes the sound of the beans for cat litter, then he poos on there instead of in his tray."

"Lovely," said David, glancing anxiously at the duvet.

With a rake of claws against fresh bed linen, Mrs Pennykettle emerged clutching a brown tabby cat. Her curls of red hair, now in total disarray, resembled a rather bedraggled mop. She grimaced in apology, plonked Bonnington on the windowsill and bundled him ungracefully into the garden.

David moved the conversation on. "Are there buses to the college from here?"

"Loads," said Lucy.

"Three an hour," her mother confirmed, hastily re-plumping her hair. "And there's room in the shed for a bike, if you have one. If you were stuck, you could always have a lift into town in my car – as long as you don't mind sharing with the dragons."

"Oh yes," said David, raising a finger. His mind floated back to the wording on the postcard in the newsagent's window: MUST LIKE CATS AND CHILDREN AND...

"Like him." Lucy pointed to a shelf above a sealed-off fireplace. Sitting at its centre was a small, clay dragon, unlike any that David had ever seen. It wasn't a fearsome, fire-breathing monster, the sort of dragon that might capture medieval maidens. Nor was it a cutesy, cartoon sort of thing. There was a fiery pride in its oval-shaped eyes as if it had a sense of its own importance and knew it had a definite place in the world. Its tall slim body was painted green with turquoise hints at the edges of its scales. It was sitting erect on two flat feet and an arrow-shaped tail that swung back on itself in a single loop. Four ridged wings (two large, two small) fanned out from its back and shoulders. A set of spiky, flag-like scales ran the entire length of its spine.

David picked it up – and very nearly dropped it. "It's warm," he said, blinking in surprise.

"That's because—"

"It's been in the sun too long," said Mrs Pennykettle, quickly cutting her daughter off. She lifted the dragon out of David's hands and rested it gently back on the shelf. A cone of sunlight fell across it.

"There are loads of dragons in our house," said Lucy, a bubble of excitement in her voice.

David smiled and touched a finger to the dragon's snout. For one strange moment he thought he could detect a layer of ash on the wide, flared nostrils. He ran a thumb across the glaze and decided it was dust. "Do you collect them?"

Lucy shook her ponytail. "We make them."

"*I* make them," said her mother.

"I'm learning," said Lucy. "*Pennykettle Pots and Crafts*. We're famous. Mum sells them at the market on Tuesday and Thursday and Saturday afternoons. When there's a craft fair at Scrubbley Garden Centre she takes some there. Lots of people buy them."

"I bet," said David, with a nod of admiration. "Do you make them here?"

Mrs Pennykettle pointed at the ceiling. "I have a small studio in one of the bedrooms."

"It's called the Dragons' Den," Lucy said mysteriously. She put her hands behind her back and swung her shoulders. "*You're* not allowed to enter."

"Lucy, don't tease," her mother chided. Turning to David again she said, "I'll gladly show you round once you've settled – well, if you decide to take the room, that is."

David ran a hand through his mop of brown hair. Dragons. It was certainly different from his last set of lodgings, where all you got were spiders and the occasional mouse. "It's perfect," he said. "Just what I want. If you and your dragons will have me, Mrs Pennykettle, I'd like to move in right away."

"Call me Liz," she said, holding out a hand. "We'd love you to stay. Wouldn't we, Lucy?"

Lucy wiggled her nose. "That depends – on the other thing."

"Other thing?" said Liz. "What other thing?"

Lucy beamed directly at David and said, "Do you like—?"

Turn the page for a taste of the second book in

The Last Dragon *Chronicles*

Icefire

Chris d'Lacey

The Wishing Dragon

"David, if your face grows any longer your chin will be scraping the soles of your shoes." Elizabeth Pennykettle hung up her apron and half-scowled, half-smiled at her student lodger. "Whatever's the matter?"

"Give you one guess," the lodger muttered cheerlessly. He sloped into the kitchen, his mouth turned down in a curve of disappointment. In his hand, he was flapping a letter. As he approached the kitchen table he pushed the letter under the snout of a dragon, which was sitting by a pot of raspberry jam. "Here, torch that."

The little clay dragon remained unmoved.

On the far side of the table Mrs Pennykettle's daughter, Lucy, tutted. "You mustn't say that to the dragons. They're not allowed to burn things, are they, Mum?"

"No," said Mrs Pennykettle, glancing at the letter. "I take it that's another rejection?"

David nodded. "Complete with coffee stain. This makes fourteen now. And they all say the same. Dear Mr Rain. Thanks, but no thanks. No one wants to hear about Snigger the squirrel."

Lucy immediately put down her sticks. She had been busy modelling a brand new dragon, a handsome (if slightly bemused-looking) creature with wide, flared nostrils and enormous paws. She picked up the letter and frowned. "Well, *I* think it's the best story *ever*."

"You're biased," said David, peeling a banana. "I wrote it for you. You're bound to say that."

"It's not a bad rejection, though, is it?" said Liz, reading the letter over Lucy's shoulder. "They do say your writing shows some promise. Perhaps you should forget about Snigger for a while and start working on something new?"

"Yes!" exclaimed Lucy, spinning in her seat. *"The Adventures of Spikey the Hedgehog."*

Through a mouthful of banana, David said: "I'm not writing about blooming hedgehogs."

"But you said Gadzooks wrote 'Spikey' on his pad. And he underlined it. Twice. Gadzooks is your *special* dragon. You've got to do what he says."

David sighed and let his gaze drift across the kitchen. It settled on the top of the fridge, where a so-called 'listening' dragon sat: a studious-looking, bespectacled creature with ears like a couple of large rose petals. Dragons were everywhere in this house; Elizabeth Pennykettle made them for a living, in a room upstairs called the Dragons' Den. Gadzooks, the dragon that Lucy had spoken of, sat on the windowsill in David's room. Liz had made him as a welcoming gift when David had first moved into the house. In general appearance, Gadzooks was like most of the Pennykettle dragons: green and scaly with oval-shaped eyes and short, ridged wings. But in his left paw he carried a small white notepad and in the right he held a sawn-off pencil. He was 'special' in the sense that, now and again, when David had been writing his squirrel story, Gadzooks had seemed to help things along by scribbling a word or two on his pad. The last thing he had 'written' – some weeks ago now – was the word 'Spikey'. Lucy had immediately decided that this must be the name of a hedgehog she had once glimpsed in the garden. But David had refused to be so easily swayed. And as the autumn days had gradually lengthened, his mind had dulled to the possibility that there was any meaning to the word at all. Indeed, if the truth be told, he was slightly tired of the presence of dragons and embarrassed by the fact that he had once allowed himself to believe that they might, in some way, be real. So when he spoke again his manner was blunt. "Lucy, let it go. I love Gadzooks, you know I do. But he only 'writes' things because I imagine him doing it. He's no more 'special' than this one you're making."

Lucy sat back, looking incensed. "This is a wishing dragon. He can make things properly happen."

Across the room there came a slight hoot of derision. But this time the dissent was not from David; it had come from the pottery expert, Liz. She walked over and inspected the dragon, looping her red hair behind her ears so it wouldn't trail into the still-soft clay. "You'll be lucky, my girl. To make a true wishing dragon takes years of practice – and careful naming. Mind you, you've not done badly with him. His paws are very good. Excellent, in fact."

"They're out of proportion, surely?" said David. "He looks like he's wearing baseball gloves. Why are they so big?"

"Because," said Lucy, drawing out the word like a piece of gum, "you put your thumbs in his paws when you make a wish. Mum, can we kiln him? Please don't say I have to squdge him. I'll think up a special name, right now." And she closed her eyes and concentrated hard. "Gurrrr..." she said, meaning the name would begin with a 'G'. "Gurrrr—"

"Reth," said David, breaking in unexpectedly.

"Gareth?" Lucy turned up her nose.

"What made you say that?" asked Liz, flipping the

handle on the outside door to let the Pennykettle's tabby cat, Bonnington, in. Bonnington trotted straight to his bowl. He sniffed at his desiccated tuna-flavoured *Chunky Chunks*, turned and mewed to go out again.

Looking puzzled, David said, "Don't know. It just came to me."

"From Gadzooks?" asked Lucy, with a sparkle in her eye.

"Yes, but he wrote it in a funny sort of way."

"Show me," said Liz, pushing a scrap of paper in front of the lodger. "Jot it down, exactly how you saw it."

So David picked up a pen and wrote:

G'reth

"You missed the 'a' out," said Lucy.

Liz turned the paper round. "No, I don't think he did. That's an archaic spelling. I've seen dragon names written that way before." She drummed her fingers on the table top. "And you saw Gadzooks do this?"

David nodded and chomped his banana. Not only had he pictured Gadzooks doing the scribble, the dragon had stomped his feet several times and thrust his pad forward, as though keen to push the name right to the forefront of David's mind.

"How do you say it?" asked Lucy.

"Guh-reth," said Liz. "With a hard 'G'. Guh."

"Guh-reth," repeated Lucy. "You say it." She gave the lodger a nudge.

"Guh-reth," he said tiredly, just to please her. He looked at the dragon with its impish smile and sent it a silent, disparaging *hrrr*.

"Lucy, try making a wish," said her mum.

Lucy's mouth fell open in astonishment. "Is it allowed? It's David's dragon."

"What?" he coughed. "I don't want it."

"You named him," said Lucy. "You have to keep him."

David shook his head. "No," he said firmly. "One dragon's enough for me."

Lucy's face took on a hurt expression. "You can't stay in this house if you don't believe in dragons."

"Yeah, well," muttered David, tossing his banana skin into the bin. He traced the grouting in the floor tiles with his toe as if he had something more to add, something he didn't want to talk about now.

Liz noticed the movement but didn't comment. "The maker may have one wish," she said, turning the dragon face-on to Lucy. "That's a rule amongst dragon-makers. It must be something beneficial and completely unselfish. You can't just wish for a bar of chocolate. If you do, the wish will turn on you."

"OK," said Lucy, resting her thumbs in G'reth's

dished paws. "I wish, I wish, I wish...it would snow."

"Snow?" hooted David. "How is that beneficial?"

"They like it," said Lucy. "Dragons like snow." As if to prove it, a gentle *hrring* sound echoed round the walls of the house.

David, who had heard this sound many times before (and had never quite got to the bottom of it) ignored the rumble and frowned in disbelief. "Why do dragons like snow? And don't tell me they're fond of skiing."

Lucy shook her head till her ponytail danced. "No one properly knows – do they, Mum?"

"No," said Liz, carefully shaping one of G'reth's wings.

"But when it does," Lucy went on excitedly, "they sit by the windows and watch it, don't they?"

"Yes," said Liz, turning G'reth back and forth on his stand. "This really is very good, Lucy. You're coming on in leaps and bounds."

"There," said Lucy, and stuck out a pimple of tongue at the lodger.

To take the wind from her sails, he gave a weather report. "Oh, bad luck. Sun's out and shining. Not a flake of snow in sight." He grinned at the Pennykettle women in turn. They stared back as if to say, 'Give it time'.

Time. David shot his watch hand up. "Oh, no!" he exclaimed. "I should have been at college *ages* ago. I'm supposed to be having a tutorial with..." Leaving the end of his sentence hanging, he shot down the hall in search of his coat.

Liz patted Lucy's arm and told her to work on G'reth a little more. "Take him up to the den when you're finished. We'll kiln him when I get back." Grabbing her car keys, she went after David. "Come on," she said, overtaking him on the porch, "if it's that important, I'll give you a lift."

On the drive into Scrubbley, Liz said quietly, "You seemed a little uptight in the kitchen. Not just about G'reth. Is there something on your mind?"

David ran the zip of his bag back and forth. "I'm meeting Sophie for dinner tonight." A smile spread slowly across his face at the mention of his girlfriend's name. "She says she wants to tell me something important. I think she might want me to move in with her."

"I see. Do you think you will?"

David bit his lip and looked the other way.

"We'll miss you," said Liz, taking his silence as a 'yes'. "It's going to be hard telling Lucy, though."

"I'll come and see you. Regularly. I promise."

Liz smiled and touched his arm. "If you need to move on, that's all there is to it. You can't stay in our mad dragon house for ever. Don't worry. We'll cope." She brought the car to a halt at the gates of Scrubbley College. "Go on, we'll talk about this another time. I hope you're not too late. Who's this chap again? The one you're having the tutorial with?"

"Dr Bergstrom. He's a polar research scientist. He's only in the country for three or four weeks, doing a sort of lecture tour."

"Bergstrom," said Liz, running the word like a spell off her tongue. "Is that Swedish?"

"Norwegian; but he works in Canada – with polar bears."

Liz nodded and lifted her gaze. Her bright green eyes seemed suddenly very distant. "Well, he won't mind this weather, then."

David turned to the windscreen.

Impossible as it seemed, it was specked with snow.

Illustration and photography copyright and permissions

Scrubbley station sign (p.10) © Chris d'Lacey

Lodgings advert (p.13) © Orchard Books

Anatomy of a Pennykettle Dragon (p.23) – © Chris d'Lacey, permitted for use by Val Chivers

Boley the polar bear (p.29) © Chris d'Lacey

The Library Gardens, Scrubbley (p.32) © Orchard Books

Val Chivers (p.39) © Chris d'Lacey, permitted for use by Val Chivers

Nutbeast collage covers (p.42) © Orchard Books

Nutbeast cartoon cover (p.43) © Tania Hunt-Newton

Letter from Megan Larkin (p.47) © Megan Larkin

Line drawings from Japanese editions (p.56, 57, 60, 61) © Take Shobo

New Walk (p.80) © Chris d'Lacey

Conker's sanctuary (p.81) © Chris d'Lacey

Scuffenbury in dragontongue (p.98) © Orchard Books

Nine bears on ice pillars (p.101) © Orchard Books

Grockle in chains (p.121) © Orchard Books

Scuffenbury Hill (p.137) © Orchard Books

Photograph of David Rain (p.140) © Marshall Pinsent

School report (p.152) © Orchard Books

Gadzooks (p.148) © Chris d'Lacey, permitted for use by Val Chivers

The Fire Within – cover of Czech Republic edition (p.159). Permitted for use by Jiri Cerny – Vydavatelstvi Vikend.

Icefire – cover of German edition (p.159). Permitted for use by Coppenwrath Verlag.

Fire Star – cover of Japanese edition (p.159). Permitted for use by Take Shobo.